SO-BZG-359

More SPLENDID LOW-CARBING

Another Splendid Guide for Low-Carbing
by Jennifer Eloff
Author of Best-selling Cookbooks
"Splendid Low-Carbing" *and*
"Splendid Desserts" *and* **"More Splendid Desserts"**

Canadian Cataloguing in Publication Data

Eloff, Jennifer, 1957
More Splendid Low-Carbing – Another Splendid Guide for Low-Carbing
First Printing ~ October 2002 Second Printing ~ August 2003
ISBN 0-7795-0034-2 Includes Index.
1. Low-carb diet recipes. 2. Sugarless recipes.
3. Desserts, cooking and baking low-carb recipes.
4. Title 5. Another Splendid Guide for Low-Carbing.

Inspiration: Thank you God from the bottom of my heart!
Photography: Ian Eloff
Front and Back Cover Design: Ian and Jonathan Eloff
Web-site Enhancements: Ian and Daniel Eloff
Printed in Canada by **Blitzprint** using Print On Demand technology

Pictured on front cover: Black Forest Cake
Pictured on back cover: Chocolate-dipped Coconut Bars, Chocolate-glazed Protein Bars, Hamburger Buns, Strawberry Chocolate Swirl Cheesecake, Barbecue Chicken Pizza, Lemon Squares, Gingersnaps, Chocolate Chip Cookies and Candy Squares.

Published by **Eureka Publishing** *Calgary*

I

CONTENTS

THE FAT FAST

This is not something I had planned for *More Splendid Low-Carbing*. It just so happened at the end of writing *More Splendid Low-Carbing*, that I discovered this amazingly effective diet plan, aptly named the "Fat Fast", by the famous Dr. Atkins. I believe God guided me in adding this section, to help others, who are struggling to lose weight even on a ketogenic diet, particularly those struggling to lose that *very stubborn last 10-15 lbs*. This has been my struggle as well.

Benoit discovered that the Fat Fast out-performed the total fast by 88%!!! The Benoit Study: For 10 days, 7 overweight guys did the fat fast. The guys that fasted lost an average of 21 pounds with 7.5 pounds of that being body fat. The guys that did the fat fast lost an average of 14.5 pounds and 14 pounds of that was body fat! The fat fast guys lost almost twice as much fat while the regular fasters lost 27 times more muscle!

For a recipe to qualify as suitable for the 75 to 80% Fat Fast, it had to be over 70% fat per serving. For a recipe to qualify as suitable for the 85 to 90% Fat Fast, it had to be over 85% fat per serving. ***Sample menus*** for the Fat Fast can be found on pages 9, 12, 14, 16, 17, 20, 28, 34 and 41. For a modified fat fast of 1200 calories, it is very simple to add a 200-calorie item to the menus. My menus are just meant as a guideline. The easiest one to follow is on page 14.

10 Pearls of wisdom re the Fat Fast:

1) Read about severe metabolic resistance to weight loss and about the Fat Fast in Dr. Atkins' New Diet Revolution book and online http://atkins.com/Archive/2001/12/21-237659.html. Try to ascertain the root cause of difficulty in losing weight, for example, hypothyroidism (see my thyroid story: http://low-carb.us/hypothyroid.html), candida (yeast), hormone therapy, medications, etc. Consult with your doctor.

2) Keep tabs on what you're eating. Estimating is doomed to failure. Induction percentages look a bit like this: 60-65% fat, 30-35% protein and 5-10% carbs. Fat Fast: 75-90% fat, 15-20% protein and 1-7% carbs. www.fitday.com is a useful site to keep track of percentages, etc.

3) The Fat Fast should not be continued longer than 5 days at a time. Keep calories between 900 to 1000 and fat between 75-90%. Four or five small "meals" a day of 250 or 200 calories are recommended. The next low-carb cookbook has an extremely useful meal replacement Fat Fast Shake.

4) Drink lots of water and take 1 tbsp (15 mL) Psyillium husks before bedtime in a full glass of water for extra fiber. Unsweetened coconut is also great for added fiber in the diet.

5) Take supplements and especially potassium, chromium, zinc, calcium and magnesium, B vitamins, folic acid and a good multi-vitamin. Enough potassium, magnesium and calcium supplementation is ultra-important to prevent muscle cramps, maintain healthy blood pressure and to keep the electrolytes balanced in the body. Potassium is contra-indicated for some blood pressure medications. Confer with your doctor.

6) It is more effective to enter a Fat Fast already in ketosis, with appetite suppression in full swing.

7) Moderate aerobic exercise and/or weight training can speed fat loss.

8) Plotting a graph of daily weight is such motivation as one can see the overall downward trend, even with the occasional hiccups.

9) Scales are not a very accurate way to measure body fat. Calculate body fat percentage to get a better idea. Take body measurements as well.

10) Remember, if the recipe is suitable for the Fat Fast, it most likely will be suitable for Induction and other levels of low-carbing.

It is common to experience headaches at first, however, if you feel bad on the Fat Fast, stop doing it and seek medical advice. Dr. Atkins did not recommend the Fat Fast for anyone other than for those individuals with severe metabolic resistance to weight loss. In the opinion of many seasoned low-carbers, the Fat Fast is a useful tool to break a stall of several months. Do exercise caution.

For those of you reading this, who feel concerned about eating all that fat, remember in the absence of lots of starchy carbohydrates, it's acceptable. Trans fats are never healthy. The Fat Fast is not a lifetime approach to eating, but simply a temporary or occasional tool in the hands of experienced dieters.

Warning: Before attempting the Fat Fast, first check with your low-carb friendly doctor. Dr. Atkins states that a modified Fat Fast of 1200 calories with more dietary supplements and 75-80% fat and the other 20% containing mostly protein, is in his opinion, safe for the metabolically resistant dieter to continue longer term. The Fat Fast is not recommended for a person who can get into ketosis easily and lose weight (even if slowly) on the Atkins diet, or any other diet for that matter, because that person could lose weight too rapidly and that can be dangerous, as blood pressure can rise due to an electrolyte imbalance (potassium depletion, especially), blood sugar can become unstable, muscle weakness and extreme fatigue can occur, etc.

HELPFUL HINTS

1.   Two new lower carb bake mixes are featured in this book. They are useful in some recipes, however, sometimes I indicate only one bake mix will be best for a particular recipe. When a recipe calls for Ultimate Bake Mix, page 67, it means either the soy or whey version will work. The book following this one will have a Nut-free Ultimate Bake Mix, which may also be substituted.

2.   It is easy to replace SPLENDA® Granular (and reduce carbs) with Da Vinci® Gourmet Sugar Free Syrup, where there is already liquid in the recipe that can be replaced. The carb breakdown for various amounts of SPLENDA® Granular may be found in *Splendid Low-Carbing*, page 19. It is possible to use other brands of Sugar Free Syrup, such as Torani's® or Nature's Flavors®. It is also possible to substitute SPLENDA® Granular with any other granulated sweetener that is suitable for baking. If liquid SPLENDA® (pure sucralose in solution) becomes available, this too may be used instead of the granular sweetener. Kool-Aid® flavoring or flavored extracts, water and SPLENDA® Granular may be used instead of sugar free syrups.

3.   All flavors of Da Vinci® Gourmet Sugar Free syrup may be purchased online at www.davincigourmet.com. United Grocers Cash and Carry in the U.S.A. carries these syrups at wholesale prices. Walmart stores carry some as well. Guar gum, xanthan gum, Bob's Red Mill vital wheat gluten (my breads typically require this product for best results) and sugar free chocolate chips, among many other products, are available from http://stores.yahoo.com/carbsmart/.Whole milk powder can be obtained from www.americanspice.com (click on "powders" and then "show all"on the page that appears). www.bobsredmill.com and www.synergydiet.com have specialty low-carb products. Most of the specialty ingredients for the recipes, including the aforementioned, may be purchased at upscale health food stores or grocery stores with a large health food section. An excellent site with research and links to online stores as well is: http://www.lowcarbsuccess.net/

4.   Skim milk powder may be used instead of whole milk powder. If skim milk powder consists of coarse granules, blend until fine in blender.

5.   Large eggs were used. Recipes may often be halved or doubled.

6.   Following are examples of recipe makeovers to lower carbs in recipes from *Splendid Desserts* and *More Splendid Desserts*. These changes will be easier for the experienced baker, as liquid needs to be added

cautiously, when using Ultimate Bake Mix, page 67, to achieve the correct batter consistency, plus in some cases improvising will be required. Some recipes will not lend themselves to a low-carb menu, however, you may find substitutes for them in my low-carb cookbooks. A good nutritional program or www.fitday.com will help calculate the nutritional analysis of recipes you yourself choose to modify.

SPLENDID DESSERTS: Chocolate Cheesecake Muffins, p. 16: *(23 g Carbs reduced to 6.7 g Carbs)* Use Ultimate Bake Mix, page 67, instead of all-purpose flour and substitute ¹/₂ cup (125 mL) whipping cream for the skim milk. Add any extra liquid in the form of water gradually, to get the right batter consistency.

White Cake, p. 27: *(26.1 g Carbs reduced to 12.1 g Carbs)* Use 1 cup (250 mL) half-and-half cream instead of skim milk and some water to make a moist batter. Replace self-raising cake flour with self-raising Ultimate Bake Mix, page 67 (keep baking powder and baking soda in recipe). Use Condensed Milk, page 88.

Glazed Blueberry Cheese Pie, p. 51: *(24.4 g Carbs reduced to 8.4 g Carbs – Yield: 10 servings)* Use Cookie Crust, page 77. For filling use 1 cup (250 mL) Ricotta cheese or full fat cottage cheese. For the topping, follow Raspberry Sauce recipe, *Splendid Low-Carbing,* page 147, substituting blueberries.

Chocolate Swirl Cheesecake, p. 41: Use a nut crust from any of my low-carb cookbooks. Use higher fat Ricotta cheese, regular or light cream cheese (same carbs typically), full cream yogurt or sour cream and soy or spelt flour.

MORE SPLENDID DESSERTS: No Bake Strawberry Cheesecake, p. 43: *(13.0 g Carbs reduced to 7.4 g Carbs)* Use Almond Crust, *Splendid Low-Carbing*, page 149. Use ¹/₂ cup (125 mL) SPLENDA® Granular, ¹/₄ cup (50 mL) Da Vinci® Sugar Free Strawberry syrup (omit water), and 1¹/₂ cups (375 mL) whipping cream, whipped.

Key Lime Pie, p. 67: *(29.8 g Carbs reduced to 9.0 g Carbs – Yield: 10 servings)* Use Almond Crust, *Splendid Low-Carbing*, page 163, Condensed Milk (not Fat Fast recipe), page 88 of this book and whole milk powder. Garnish pie with Crème Fraiche, page 70.

Chocolate Coconut Squares, p. 106: *(4.3 g Carbs reduced to 1.4 g Carbs)* Use ²/₃ cup (150 mL) Condensed Milk (not Fat Fast recipe), page 88. Omit fructose. (65.1 calories, 1.1 g protein, 5.7 g fat (78.0%), 1.4 g carbs)

Tangy Lemon Creams, p. 100: *(10.6 g Carbs reduced to 4.6 g Carbs – 2 cookies per serving)* Use Ultimate Bake Mix, page 67, instead of all-purpose flour. Use regular sour cream, cottage cheese and cream cheese.

BEVERAGES

HOT CHOCOLATE
A comfort drink.

1 tbsp cocoa (15 mL)
$^{1}/_{4}$ cup whipping cream (50 mL)
$^{1}/_{4}$ cup Da Vinci® Sugar Free (50 mL)
  Chocolate syrup

Yield: 1 serving
1 serving
190.6 calories
2.3 g protein
19.5 g fat
2.5 g carbs

In cup, place cocoa. Gradually whisk in whipping cream. Stir in syrup and water to fill cup. Microwave 1 minute, stir and enjoy. Add SPLENDA® Granular to taste, if desired.

Helpful Hint: **85-90% Fat Fast:** 1 serving. (85.5%)

CHOCOLATE PROTEIN SHAKE
Deliciously, smooth shake.

$^{1}/_{4}$ cup whipping cream (50 mL)
$^{1}/_{4}$ cup ice cold water (50 mL)
$^{1}/_{3}$ cup Chocolate Whey Protein (75 mL)
2 tbsp DaVinci® Sugar Free (25 mL)
  Chocolate Syrup, OR 1 SPLENDA®
  packet
2 blocks ice

Yield: 1 cup (250 mL)
$^{1}/_{2}$ cup (125 mL) per serving
136.5 calories
9.2 g protein
10.2 g fat
2.2 g carbs

In blender, combine whipping cream, water, Chocolate Whey Protein, DaVinci® Sugar Free Chocolate Syrup or SPLENDA® packet and ice. Blend.

GINGER BEER

This idea came from Sandra Van Harten. I love it, as it is so easy to make.

6¼ cups water (1.5 L)
4 oz fresh ginger root (120 g)
1 cup SPLENDA® Granular (250 mL)

Yield: 12 servings
1 serving
0.8 calories
0.0 g protein
0.0 g fat
2.0 g carbs

In large saucepan, place water. Peel ginger, cut into large pieces and chop finely in food processor or blender. Add ginger to water. Bring to boil and simmer 10 minutes. Allow to cool. Pour into jug and refrigerate overnight. Sieve. Stir in SPLENDA® Granular. Pour about ½ cup (125 mL) ginger syrup in a tall glass and add 1 cup (250 mL) ice cold lemon-lime carbonated spring water. Enjoy!

Variation: **Ginger Herbal Tea:** Add 3 tbsp (45 mL) ginger syrup to a cup. Fill with water and heat in microwave oven 1 minute. Serve with a slice of lemon, if desired. (*0.8 g Carbs*)

CRANBERRY ICED TEA

*For an even lower carb drink, consider replacing the sweetener with Da Vinci®
Sugar Free Raspberry or Strawberry syrup (0.6 g Carbs).*

1 cup water (250 mL)
2 cranberry tea bags
3 cups ice cold water (750 mL)
⅓ cup SPLENDA® Granular (75 mL)
⅓ cup Cranberry Cocktail juice (75 mL)
   (sweetened with sucralose)

Yield: 4 cups (1 L)
1 cup (250 mL) per serving
10.4 calories
0.0 g protein
0.0 g fat
2.6 g carbs

In medium saucepan, bring 1 cup (250 mL) water to boiling. Turn off heat. Add 2 cranberry tea bags; leave in 5 minutes. Remove tea bags. To large juice container, add tea, cold water, SPLENDA® Granular and Cranberry Cocktail juice; stir. Serve over crushed ice or ice cubes.

LEMONADE CONCENTRATE

A handy recipe!

2 cups cold lemon juice (500 mL)

2 cups SPLENDA® Granular (500 mL)

$^{1}/_{2}$ cup ice cold water (125 mL)

Yield: 24 servings
1 serving
13.1 calories
0.1 g protein
0.0 g fat
3.7 g carbs

In juice jug, combine lemon juice, SPLENDA® Granular and cold water. Chill. Use 2 tbsp (25 mL) Lemonade Concentrate in a large glass and fill with 8 oz (250 mL) ice cold water.

CRANBERRY COCKTAIL CONCENTRATE

A light pink, pretty drink. This is a good alternative for those people who cannot tolerate the high acidity of the Lemonade Concentrate. Cranberry juice is reportedly very good for women for gynecological reasons.

2 cups Cranberry Cocktail juice (500 mL)
  (sucralose-sweetened)

2 cups SPLENDA® Granular (500 mL)

$^{1}/_{4}$ cup lemon juice, from (50 mL)
  concentrate

Yield: $2^{1}/_{2}$ cups (550 mL)
2 tbsp (25 mL) per serving
13.4 calories
0.0 g protein
0.0 g fat
3.4 g carbs

In large juice jug, combine Cranberry Cocktail juice, SPLENDA® Granular and lemon juice. Use 2 tbsp (25 mL) concentrate and add ice-cold water or carbonated water to taste.

~~Low-Carb Dieting Tip~~

Low-Carbing is recommended for folks who have hypothyroidism, as it is known to balance the body's hormonal needs.

APPETIZERS

SPICED PECAN CLUSTERS

Addictive, delightfully light, crispy pecans! Our sons' favorite is the variation below. Place these clusters in a pretty tin lined with wax paper for a thoughtful holiday gift.

1 egg white
$^1/_2$ cup SPLENDA® Granular (125 mL)
$^3/_4$ tsp salt (3 mL)
1 tsp ground cinnamon (5 mL)
$^1/_4$ tsp ground nutmeg (1 mL)
$^1/_8$ tsp ground cloves (0.5 mL)
2 cups pecan halves (500 mL)

Yield: 8 servings	
1 serving	
197.5 calories	
2.2 g protein	
19.3 g fat	
5.1 g carbs	

In medium bowl, beat egg white with fork until foamy. Blend in SPLENDA® Granular, salt, cinnamon, nutmeg and cloves. Add nuts, stirring until coated well. Spread nuts out on greased cookie sheet. Make sure nuts touch, clustering together, so that they can be broken off later in little clusters.

Bake in 325°F (160°C) oven 20 minutes. Remove immediately from cookie sheet in clusters and allow to cool on wire rack.

Variation: **Cinnamon Pecans:** For spices, use $1^1/_2$ tsp (7 mL) cinnamon and $^1/_8$ tsp (0.5 mL) salt.

Helpful Hints: This recipe may be doubled and the pecans will still fit on one cookie sheet.

75-80% Fat Fast: 1 serving.
(197.5 calories, 2.2 g protein, 19.3 g fat (82.5%), 5.1 g carbs)

~~Low-Carb Dieting Tip~~
Drink plenty of water regularly throughout the day.

CHEDDAR TACO CHIPS

Excellent replacement for taco chips in appetizers. These are awesome in Taco Salad, page 20. Make as many batches as you require.

1.2 oz grated cheddar cheese (34 g)
$1^1/_2$ tsp vital wheat gluten (7 mL)
$^1/_2$ tsp light-tasting olive oil (2 mL)

> **Yield:** 1 serving (1 chip)
> 1 serving
> 21.5 calories
> 1.4 g protein
> 1.7 g fat
> ***0.1 g carbs***

Using an electronic scale, weigh cheese. Sprinkle cheese in 5-inch (13 cm) nonstick pan (basically cheese just covers surface). As cheese melts over medium heat, sprinkle vital wheat gluten evenly over top. Drizzle with olive oil overall. Cook just until it can flip (use spatula and fork simultaneously for control). Cook a few seconds on other side. Scrape any excess gluten off underside. Wipe pan clean with paper towel inbetween batches. Cut in half while still warm and then cut each half into 4 taco chip triangular shapes. Place last cooked side face down on ungreased cookie sheet, making sure chips do not touch each other. Bake in 350°F (180°C) oven 10 minutes.

Helpful Hints: If you do not have an electronic scale, keep the following in mind: grated cheese just barely covers the surface of the pan. My electronic scale is a Danescook® 907/2, and measures in ounces and grams.

75-80% Fat Fast: 10 chips per serving.
(215 calories, 14 g protein, 17 g fat, (70.9%) 1 g carbs)

Menu #1 75 to 80% Fat Fast	Calories	Protein	Fat	Carbs	% Fat
Strawberry Milk Shake, SLC p. 16	135.0	1.9	12.8	2.5	85.5
French Omelet, SLC	234.2	13.0	19.2	1.9	74.3
p. 38 with 1 oz (30 g) Cheddar Cheese	114.1	7.1	9.4	0.4	74.0
Chicken & Spicy Avo. Dress., SLC p. 31	268.0	15.6	21.4	3.4	70.7
Avocado Walnut Salad, SLC p. 34	185.2	3.0	17.5	5.2	79.7
TOTAL	**936.5**	**40.6**	**80.3**	**13.4**	**76.8**

BUFFALO WINGS

This is a favorite for many. Here is my version.

$^1/_3$ cup tomato paste (75 mL)
3 tbsp white vinegar (45 mL)
2 tbsp SPLENDA® Granular (25 mL)
2 tbsp Tabasco sauce (25 mL)
$^1/_4$ tsp salt (1 mL)
3 lbs chicken wings (1.4 kg)

> **Yield:** 8 servings
> 1 serving
> 388.6 calories
> 31.6 g protein
> 27.3 g fat
> ***1.9 g carbs***

In small bowl, combine tomato paste, vinegar, SPLENDA® Granular, Tabasco sauce and salt. Brush wings with sauce on both sides. Place on greased foil-lined cookie sheet. Bake in 350°F (180°C) oven 45 minutes. Brown 6 inches (15 cm) under broiler 5 minutes. Watch carefully during last minute to prevent burning wings.

Helpful Hint: Increase heat by adding an extra tbsp (15 mL) Tabasco sauce.

HORSERADISH SHRIMP DIP

Serve this dip with salad shrimp hung decoratively over side of a dip bowl.

$^1/_2$ cup Mayonnaise, page 58 (125 mL)
2 tbsp tomato paste (25 mL)
1 tbsp lemon juice (15 mL)
1 tbsp prepared horseradish (15 mL)
1 tsp SPLENDA® Granular (5 mL)
$^1/_4$ tsp hot chili powder (1 mL)

> **Yield:** $^3/_4$ cup (175 mL)
> 1 tsp (5 mL) per serving
> 22.5 calories
> 0.1 g protein
> 2.4 g fat
> ***0.3 g carbs***

In small bowl, combine Mayonnaise, page 58, tomato paste, lemon juice, horseradish, SPLENDA® Granular and chili powder. Stir well.

Helpful Hints: Serve with a few shrimp and/or raw induction-style veggies.

85-90% Fat Fast: 10 tsp (50 mL) per serving.
(225 calories, 1 g protein, 24 g fat (91.9%), 3 g carbs)

SESAME HAM ROLL

This spread is great on low-carb crackers, page 126 of Splendid Low-Carbing.

8 oz regular cream cheese, (250 g)
  softened
$1^1/_2$ cups chopped, canned ham (375 mL)
2 tbsp finely chopped green onion (25 mL)
1 tsp Worcestershire sauce (5 mL)
1 tsp lemon juice (5 mL)
1 tsp dried parsley (5 mL)
3 tbsp toasted sesame seeds (45 mL)

Yield: 36 servings
1 serving
32.3 calories
1.6 g protein
2.7 g fat
0.6 g carbs

In food processor, process cream cheese until smooth. Stir in ham, green onion, Worcestershire sauce, lemon juice and parsley. On oblong platter, form into log shape about 11 inches (28 cm) long and 2 inches (5 cm) wide. Sprinkle with sesame seeds. Refrigerate until firm. Slice and serve with low-carb crackers or spread on cucumber slices or celery sticks.

***Helpful Hint:* 75-80% Fat Fast:** 8 servings.
(256 calories, 12.8 g protein, 21.6 g fat (73.0%), 4.8 g carbs)

ZESTY VEGGIE DIP

Delicious dip for veggies with bits of green pepper showing through.

4 oz light cream cheese, (125 g)
  softened
$^1/_4$ cup whipping cream (50 mL)
$^1/_2$ cup Thousand Island Dressing (125 mL)
  Splendid Low-Carbing, page 100
1 tbsp Tabsco Sauce (15 mL)

Yield: $1^1/_4$ cups (300 mL)
1 tsp (5 mL) serving
18.2 calories
0.2 g protein
1.9 g fat
0.2 g carbs

In food processor with sharp blade, blender or in bowl with electric mixer, process cream cheese and whipping cream until smooth. Add Thousand Island Dressing, *Splendid Low-Carbing*, page 100 and Tabasco sauce; process. Scoop into dipping bowl.

Helpful Hint: If using commercial Thousand Island Dressing, add finely chopped green pepper to food processor.

85-90% Fat Fast: 10 tsp (50 mL) per serving.
(182.0 calories, 2.0 g protein, 19.0 g fat (91.0%), 2.0 g carbs)

CURRIED CHICKEN PUFFS

A bit of work is required for these tasty puffs, but well worth the effort.

Puffs:
1 cup water (250 mL)
$^1/_2$ cup butter (125 mL)
$^1/_8$ tsp salt (0.5 mL)
$1^1/_2$ cups Whey Ultimate Bake (375 mL)
  Mix, page 67
2 eggs

Curried Chicken:
$^1/_2$ cup sour cream (125 mL)
2 tbsp Ranch dressing (25 mL)
1 tsp SPLENDA® Granular (5 mL)
$1^1/_2$ tsp prepared mustard (7 mL)
1 tsp Curry powder, page 61, OR to taste (5 mL)
2 cups cubed cooked chicken (500 mL)

Yield: 16 puffs
1 serving
144.6 calories
9.7 g protein
10.0 g fat
3.6 g carbs

Puffs: Spray cookie sheet with nonstick cooking spray; set aside. In medium saucepan, combine water, butter and salt; bring to boil. Stir in Whey Ultimate Bake Mix all at once. Stir in eggs one at a time, beating with wooden spoon after each addition until smooth.

Spoon into pastry bag with $^1/_2$–inch (1 cm) front opening; secure bag with ring, if necessary. Pipe sixteen 2-inch (5 cm) rounds onto prepared cookie sheet. Bake in 450°F (230°C) oven 15 minutes. Reduce heat to 350°F (180°C) and bake a further 10 minutes or until puffed and golden brown. Cool completely on wire rack. Split in half and remove soft dough from inside. Fill each with curried chicken and replace tops. Serve cold or put back in oven on cookie sheet 8 minutes, or until warm, if desired.

Curried Chicken: In small bowl, combine sour cream, Ranch dressing, SPLENDA® Granular, mustard and Curry powder, page 61. Stir in chicken.

Menu #2 75 to 80% Fat Fast	Calories	Protein	Fat	Carbs	%Fat
Hot Choc., SLC p. 15	190.6	2.3	19.5	2.5	85.5
Shrimp Spread & ½ cup cucumber p. 12	234.7	6.4	22.5	2.3	88.1
Chunky Egg Salad, p. 19	254.8	10.2	22.5	2.7	79.4
Taco Dog, p. 35	251.3	13.2	20.1	4.3	71.5
TOTAL	**931.4**	**32.1**	**84.6**	**11.8**	**81.1**

SHRIMP SPREAD

My husband likes this spread on Wasa® Crackers and he even likes it "nuked" on the cracker.

$^1/_2$ cup Mayonnaise, page 58 (125 mL)
$^1/_2$ cup butter, softened (125 mL)
2 cans cocktail shrimp (2 x 106 g)
2 tbsp finely chopped onion (25 mL)
1 tbsp lemon juice (15 mL)
$^1/_8$ tsp garlic powder (0.5 mL)
$^1/_8$ tsp onion salt (0.5 mL)

> **Yield:** 2 cups (500 mL)
> 1 tbsp (15 mL) per serving
> 56.9 calories
> 1.5 g protein
> 5.6 g fat
> *0.3 g carbs*

In medium bowl, combine Mayonnaise, page 58 butter, cocktail shrimp, onion, lemon juice, garlic powder and onion salt. Chill. Serve with low-carb crackers or rye crisp breads.

Variation: **Toast Cups with Shrimp Spread:** Use 3 slices low-carb bread of choice. Cut crusts off each slice. Cut each slice into four squares. Using a mini muffin pan, press each square into ungreased muffin cups. Bake in 350°F (180°C) oven on bottom rack 15 minutes, or until edges are browned. Invert muffin pan. Allow toast cups to cool completely. To store, place in sealed plastic bag. These may be used for a variety of fillings, or serve shrimp spread with mini toast cups piled around it and small butter knives for guests. *Yield:* 12 toast cups. Carbs will vary depending on low-carb bread used. Divide carbs for each slice bread by 4.

Helpful Hint: **85-90% Fat Fast:** Serve $^1/_4$ cup (50 mL) Shrimp Spread on approximately $^1/_2$ cup (125 mL) sliced cucumber. (analysis with cucumber) (234.7 calories, 6.4 g protein, 22.5 g fat (88.1%), 2.3 g carbs)

~~Low-Carb Dieting Tip~~
Vegetables are our new best friends – enjoy a wide variety.

SOUPS AND SALADS

CHILI ITALIAN-STYLE

This chili is actually meant to be served without kidney beans!

1 lb lean ground beef (0.454 kg)
$^1/_2$ cup chopped onion (125 mL)
23 fl oz Classico® Spicy Red Pepper
  Sauce, or similar tomato sauce (680 mL)
$1^1/_2$ cups water (375 mL)
1, 14 oz can sliced mushrooms, (284 mL)
  drained
2 oz chopped pepperoni (60 g)
2 tbsp tomato paste (25 mL)
1 tbsp instant beef stock mix (15 mL)
$^1/_2$ tsp hot chili powder, OR to taste (2 mL)

Yield: 8 servings
1 serving
192.7 calories
13.7 g protein
11.9 g fat
6.6 g carbs

In large electric frying pan or nonstick saucepan, brown beef and onions. Pour off fat. Stir in Classico® Spicy Red Pepper Sauce, water, mushrooms, pepperoni, tomato paste, beef stock mix and hot chili powder. Bring to boil, reduce heat and simmer uncovered about half an hour.

Menu #3 (easy!) 75 to 80% Fat Fast	Calories	Protein	Fat	Carbs	%Fat
Mock Danish, p. 26	248.4	8.5	22.9	2.2	82.9
Choc. Peanut Butter	236.4	7.7	22.0	2.9	82.6
Delight, p. 26					
2 Hard boiled eggs	300.7	13.3	26.0	2.9	77.8
½ cup cucumber					
1½ tbsp (22 mL)					
mayonaise page 58					
¼ cup (50 mL)	242.1	3.5	24.3	3.4	88.8
whipping cream					
in tea/coffee during					
the day, plus 2 tsp					
(5 mL) peanut butter					
for a snack					
TOTAL	**1027.6**	**33.0**	**95.2**	**11.4**	**83.0**

HAMBURGER SOUP

A hearty, delicious soup, which can easily be doubled to feed a crowd.

1 lb lean ground beef (0.454 kg)
$^1/_2$ cup chopped onion (125 mL)
$4^1/_2$ cups water (1.125 L)
1 cup coarsely chopped cabbage (250 mL)
1 cup sliced mushrooms (250 mL)
$^1/_2$ cup tomato sauce (125 mL)
4 envelopes beef bouillon (60 mL)
1 bay leaf
$^1/_2$ green pepper, chopped
$^1/_2$ red pepper, chopped
$^1/_4$ tsp salt (1 mL)
$^1/_4$ tsp black pepper (1 mL)
$^1/_4$ tsp hot chili powder (1 mL)

Yield: 6 generous servings
1 serving
188.7 calories
15.3 g protein
11.6 g fat
4.5 g carbs

In deep saucepan, brown beef and onion; pour off fat. Stir in water, cabbage, mushrooms, tomato sauce, beef bouillon, bay leaf, green pepper, red pepper, salt, pepper and chili powder. Bring to boil, reduce heat and boil gently, covered, 20 minutes, or until vegetables are tender. Sprinkle with cheese, if desired.

CREAM OF AVOCADO SOUP

Served warm, this simple avocado soup is my favorite!

$2^3/_4$ cups water (675 mL)
1 tbsp dehydrated onion, (15 mL)
  (minced)
1 tbsp instant chicken stock mix (15 mL)
3 avocadoes
$^3/_4$ cup whipping cream (175 mL)
$^1/_4$ tsp salt, OR to taste (1 mL)
$^1/_2$ tsp white pepper (2 mL)
$^1/_2$ tsp lemon juice (2 mL)
Avocado slice for garnish, (optional)

Yield: 6 servings.
$^3/_4$ cup (175 ml) plus
246.1 calories
2.5 g protein
24.6 g fat
5.2 g carbs

In medium saucepan, combine water, onion and instant chicken stock mix. Bring to boil and simmer a few minutes, or until onion is tender. Peel and chop avocadoes. Place in blender; pour in chicken stock and puree. Return to saucepan (not over heat), stirring in cream. Place over low heat. Add salt and pepper. Heat soup to scalding, but do not boil. Stir in lemon juice. Serve immediately, garnished with avocado slices, if desired.

Helpful Hint: **75-80% Fat Fast:** 1 serving. (82.8% fat)

DELUXE EGG DROP SOUP

If you like spinach, this soup can be a lovely way to get your salad greens during induction on a cold, wintry day. It's filling, warm and satisfying with few calories and practically negligible carbs!

2 tsp olive oil (10 mL)
1 clove garlic, crushed
4 cups water (1 L)
10 oz frozen chopped spinach (300 g)
2 tbsp instant chicken stock mix (25 mL)
1 cup diced, cooked chicken (250 mL)
1 extra-large egg, fork beaten
1 tsp lemon juice (5 mL)
$^1/_4$ tsp black pepper (1 mL)
4 tsp Parmesan cheese (20 mL)

> *Yield:* 4 servings
> 1 serving
> 115.4 calories
> 11.1 g protein
> 6.6 g fat
> *1.3 g carbs*

In large saucepan, heat oil and stir-fry garlic briefly. Add water, spinach and chicken stock mix. Bring water to boil and use fork to separate spinach. Simmer covered 15 minutes, stirring occasionally. Add cooked chicken and simmer 5 more minutes. Remove from heat. Slowly pour beaten egg in thin stream into soup, stirring gently. Stir in lemon juice and black pepper. Sprinkle each serving with Parmesan cheese.

Helpful Hint: If using thawed spinach (undrained), simply bring to boil, stirring occasionally and do not simmer 15 minutes. Continue recipe as directed.

Menu #4 75 to 80% Fat Fast	Calories	Protein	Fat	Carbs	%Fat
Ham & Cheese Quiche, p.24	259.7	12.4	22.5	2.3	77.5
Zucchini Tomato Bake, p. 54	144.0	4.0	12.3	3.9	73.6
Zesty Veggie Dip, p. 11 with Taco Chips	182.0	2.0	19.0	2.0	91.0
Ched.Taco Chips, p. 9	215.0	14.0	17.0	1.0	70.9
Choc. Fudge Chsck, p. 80	199.7	5.9	17.7	4.9	77.6
TOTAL	1000.4	38.3	88.5	14.1	78.1

APPLE BACON SALAD

A lovely salad. Who says we can't enjoy apple occasionally?

6 cups torn spinach, OR Romaine (1.5 L)
  lettuce
4 slices bacon, cooked & crumbled
1 apple
1 green onion, chopped
$^1/_2$ avocado, peeled & chopped

Dressing:
$^1/_2$ cup Mayonnaise, page 58 (125 mL)
$^1/_2$ cup plain yogurt (125 mL)
1 small garlic clove, crushed,
  (optional)
1 tbsp vinegar (15 mL)
1 tsp SPLENDA® Granular (5 mL)
$^1/_4$ tsp onion salt (1 mL)
$^1/_4$ tsp dry mustard (1 mL)
$^1/_8$ tsp black pepper (0.5 mL)

Yield: 6 servings
1 serving
241.1 calories
6.9 g protein
20.8 g fat
5.7 g carbs

In large bowl, combine spinach and bacon. Peel and core apple. Slice into 22 thin wedges and cut each in half. Add to salad, along with green onion and avocado. In small bowl, combine Mayonnaise, page 58, yogurt, garlic (if using), vinegar, SPLENDA® Granular, onion salt, dry mustard and black pepper. Refrigerate until serving time. Just before serving, toss salad with dressing.

Helpful Hint: **75-80% Fat Fast:** 1 serving.
(Omit apple, use 1 whole avocado and replace yogurt with sour cream.)
(255.7 calories, 7.2 g protein, 23.5 g fat (79.3%), 4.2 g carbs)

Menu #5 **75 to 80% Fat Fast**	Calories	Protein	Fat	Carbs	%Fat
Cream Cheese Scram. Eggs, SLC p. 39	154.1	7.7	13.0	1.4	76.1
Chicken Wing Drumettes, SLC p. 66	407.1	25.3	32.6	1.9	72.8
Mushroom Mozzarella Bake, p. 54	127.3	4.6	11.0	3.1	74.0
Seasoned Fried Tomatoes, SLC p. 86	129.0	2.0	12.7	2.3	85.1
Crmy Delight Orange Mousse, SLC p. 136	221.1	3.4	21.8	4.0	86.9
TOTAL	**1038.6**	**43.0**	**91.1**	**12.7**	**79.0**

MANDARIN SPINACH SALAD

I often take this salad along to parties and it's always a hit!

8 cups torn Spinach, OR Romaine (2 L)
   lettuce
2 green onions, finely chopped
1 avocado, peeled and sliced
10 oz can mandarin oranges (284 mL)
   in juice, drained
$^1/_2$ cup sliced, peeled cucumber (125 mL)
$^1/_4$ cup sunflower seeds (50 mL)
3 tbsp slivered almonds (45 mL)
Dressing:
$^1/_4$ cup light-tasting olive oil (50 mL)
3 tbsp SPLENDA® Granular (45 mL)
1 tbsp red wine vinegar (15 mL)
1 tbsp white vinegar (15 mL)
2 tsp lemon juice (10 mL)
$^1/_4$ tsp dry mustard (1 mL)
$^1/_8$ tsp salt (0.5 mL)

Yield: 8 servings
1 serving
171.0 calories
3.7 g protein
14.6 g fat
6.3 g carbs

In large salad bowl, toss spinach, green onions, avocado, mandarin oranges, cucumber, sunflower seeds and almonds. In small bowl, combine olive oil, SPLENDA® Granular, red wine vinegar, white vinegar, lemon juice, mustard and salt. Pour over salad and toss to combine. Serve immediately or toss with dressing just before serving salad.

Variation: Add sliced, grilled chicken.

Helpful Hints: When taking this salad along to a function, prepare as directed just before leaving the house, however, toss sliced avocado in lemon juice before adding. Take dressing along separately in container and toss just before serving.

75-80% Fat Fast: 1 serving without mandarin oranges.
(159.4 calories, 3.5 g protein, 14.6 g fat (76.9%), 3.6 g carbs)

Avocado Spinach Salad:
1 serving with 2 avocadoes.
(199.9 calories, 4.0 g protein, 18.5 g fat (77.2%), 4.8 g carbs)

SESAME STRAWBERRY SALAD

Delicious sweet-sour dressing with sesame seeds! Sometimes I add avocado.

8 cups torn spinach, OR Romaine (1.5 L)
  lettuce
2 cups strawberries, sliced (500 mL)
Sweet-sour Dressing:
$\frac{1}{2}$ cup light-tasting olive oil (125 mL)
$\frac{1}{2}$ cup SPLENDA® Granular (125 mL)
$\frac{1}{4}$ cup Worcestershire sauce (50 mL)
3 tbsp sesame seeds (45 mL)
2 tbsp white vinegar (25 mL)
2 tbsp cider vinegar (25 mL)
$\frac{1}{4}$ tsp paprika (1 mL)

> *Yield:* 8 servings
> 1 serving
> 175.3 calories
> 3.0 g protein
> 15.5 g fat
> *5.7 g carbs*

In large bowl, combine spinach and strawberries. In medium bowl, combine olive oil, SPLENDA® Granular, Worcestershire sauce, sesame seeds, white vinegar, cider vinegar and paprika. Before serving, toss salad with dressing.

Helpful Hint: **75-80% Fat Fast:** 1 serving (use only $1\frac{3}{4}$ cups (425 mL) strawberries). (173.8 calories, 3.0 g protein, 15.5 g fat (76.2%) 5.4 g carbs)

CHUNKY EGG SALAD

A good old stand-by.

$\frac{1}{3}$ cup Mayonnaise, page 58 (75 mL)
2 tbsp sour cream (25 mL)
1 tbsp white vinegar (15 mL)
$\frac{1}{2}$ tsp salt (2 mL)
$\frac{1}{2}$ tsp Worcestershire sauce (2 mL)
$\frac{1}{4}$ tsp white pepper (1 mL)
6 hard boiled eggs, chopped
$\frac{1}{2}$ cup finely chopped cucumber (125 mL)
2 tbsp finely chopped green onion (25 mL)
2 tbsp finely chopped red pepper (25 mL)

> *Yield:* 4 servings
> 1 serving
> 254.8 calories
> 10.2 g protein
> 22.5 g fat
> *2.7 g carbs*

In small bowl, combine Mayonnaise, page 58, sour cream, vinegar, salt, Worcestershire sauce and pepper. In another small bowl, combine egg, cucumber, green onion and red pepper. Pour mayonnaise mixture over egg-vegetable mixture. Toss to combine. Serve on lettuce leaves and garnish with fresh parsley, if desired.

Helpful Hint: **75-80% Fat Fast:** 1 serving. (79.4% fat)

TACO SALAD

This is a whole meal deal on it's own. Very similar to the traditional favorite!

1 lb lean ground beef (0.454 kg)
2 tbsp dehydrated onion flakes (25 mL)
2 tsp ground cumin (10 mL)
$^3/_4$ tsp hot chili powder (3 mL)
$^1/_2$ tsp salt (2 mL)
$^1/_2$ tsp garlic powder (2 mL)
$^1/_8$ tsp Thickening Agent, page 60 (0.5 mL)
1 cup water (250 mL)
6 cups shredded lettuce (1.5L)
1 large tomato, diced finely
$^1/_2$ cup cheddar cheese (125 mL)
$^3/_4$ cup Thousand Island Dressing, (175 mL)
   Splendid Low-Carbing, page 100
Cheddar Taco Chips, page 9

Yield: 6 servings
1 serving
408.2 calories
26.4 g protein
31.3 g fat
4.2 g carbs

In large frying pan, brown ground beef. Pour off fat. Add onion flakes, cumin, hot chili powder, salt, garlic powder and Thickening Agent, page 60. Stir in water. Bring to boil, reduce heat and simmer until sauce thickens and onion is soft.

Prepare Taco Chips as described on page 9. Prepare each plate individually. Place lettuce on plate, mound ground beef in center, diced tomato, sprinkling of cheese, and 2 tbsp (25 mL) dressing. Toss salad to mix well and arrange Taco chips on or around salad.

Helpful Hint: It is customary to toss the Taco Salad, however, it may be served without tossing, as it looks more attractive, in my opinion. Sprinkle dressing around perimeter of meat and on salad greens.

Menu #6 75 to 80% Fat Fast	Calories	Protein	Fat	Carbs	%Fat
Breakfast Squares, SLC p. 41	214.4	12.5	17.1	2.1	72.5
Moussaka, SLC p. 50	252.6	9.0	22.7	3.2	79.8
Creamy Strawberry Popsicle, SLC p. 135	86.8	1.6	7.4	2.9	79.1
Linda's Ice Cream Custard, p. 71	177.0	2.5	18.1	1.8	90.5
Quiche Lorraine, SLC p. 37	196.3	5.8	18.6	1.9	84.5
TOTAL	**927.1**	**31.4**	**83.9**	**11.9**	**81.3**

CAESAR SALAD

A classic and perfect for low-carbers! Just hold the croutons, unless you make croutons from Splendid Low-Carbing, page 110.

$^{1}/_{4}$ cup olive oil (50 mL)
*1 extra-large egg, coddled
1 clove garlic, crushed
2 tbsp lemon juice (25 mL)
1 tsp prepared mustard (5 mL)
1 tsp Worcestershire sauce (5 mL)
$^{1}/_{4}$ tsp salt (1 mL)
$^{1}/_{8}$ tsp black pepper (0.5 mL)
6 cups shredded Romaine lettuce (1.5 L)
$^{1}/_{3}$ cup Parmesan cheese (75 mL)
6 slices crisp, cooked bacon, crumbled
  (optional)

Yield: 6 servings
1 serving
129.8 calories
4.5 g protein
11.6 g fat
1.3 g carbs

In blender, combine olive oil, egg, garlic, lemon juice, mustard, Worcestershire sauce, salt and pepper; blend. Toss lettuce with Parmesan cheese and bacon bits, if using. Pour dressing over salad just before serving and toss again to coat well. Serve immediately.

Helpful Hints: "Coddled" means to cook egg in boiling water barely 1 minute.

75-80% Fat Fast: 2 servings without bacon.
(259.6 calories, 9 g protein, 23.2 g fat (79.1%), 2.6 g carbs)

TUNA SALAD FOR ONE

I like the addition of avocado as well as the crunchy vegetables.

$2^{1}/_{2}$ oz drained tuna in water (75 g)
$^{1}/_{2}$ cup chopped cucumber (125 mL)
$^{1}/_{4}$ avocado, sliced
1 radish, chopped
2 tbsp Mayonnaise, page 58 (25 mL)

Yield: 1 serving
1 serving
370.2 calories
22.4 g protein
29.3 g fat (70.2%)
3.8 g carbs

In small bowl combine tuna, cucumber, sliced avocado and chopped radish. Stir in Mayonnaise, page 58 until well combined. Serve immediately.

BREAKFAST

CINNAMON 'N CREAM WAFFLES

Very good with Crème Fraiche, page 70 and raspberries, blueberries or sliced strawberries or peaches. Drizzle with Da Vinci® Sugar Free Pancake syrup.

1 cup Protein Bake Mix, OR (250 mL)
  Whey Bake Mix, page 68
3 SPLENDA® packets
1 tbsp baking powder (15 mL)
1 tsp cinnamon (5 mL)
3 eggs, fork beaten
$^1/_2$ cup whipping cream (125 mL)
$^1/_4$ cup water (50 mL)
$^1/_3$ cup butter, melted (75 mL)

Yield: 10 waffles
1 waffle/PBM/WBM
167.9/157.1 calories
9.6 g/6.1 g protein
13.7 g/13.4 g fat
2.7 g/3.4 g carbs

Plug waffle iron in and warm up. In medium bowl, combine Protein or Whey Bake Mix, page 68, SPLENDA®, baking powder and cinnamon. In small bowl, combine eggs, whipping cream, water and butter. Stir into dry ingredients until moist and well combined.

Place 3 tbsp (45 mL) batter in center of each waffle impression. Bake according to manufacturer's directions until well browned and properly toasted. Serve immediately. If eating later, toast briefly in toaster before serving.

Variation: **Buttermilk Waffles:** Use $^3/_4$ cup (175 mL) buttermilk. Omit whipping cream and water. Add $^1/_2$ tsp (2 mL) vanilla extract. (*2.6 g/3.3 g Carbs*)

~~Low-Carb Dieting Tip~~
To beat cravings, reach for a high fat item such as cream cheese.

BARBO'S CREPES

These jumbo crepes are bound to please! These crepes freeze well.

5 large eggs
$^1/_2$ cup water (125 mL)
$^1/_2$ cup whipping cream (125 mL)
$^1/_2$ cup Ultimate Bake Mix, (125 mL)
 page 67
$^1/_4$ cup butter, melted (50 mL)
$^1/_4$ cup SPLENDA® Granular (50 mL)
$^1/_2$ tsp vanilla extract (2 mL)
$^1/_4$ tsp salt (1 mL)

Yield: 12 jumbo crepes
1 jumbo crepe
115.8 calories
4.1 g protein
10.1 g fat
2.2 g carbs

In blender, place eggs, water, whipping cream, Ultimate Bake Mix, page 67, butter, SPLENDA® Granular, vanilla extract and salt. Blend until smooth.

Heat 8-inch (20 cm) nonstick frying pan with a little butter. Pour $^1/_4$ cup (50 mL) batter into skillet and tilt until batter stops moving. Cook until bubbles form on top and it looks firm. Then pry edges up and flip carefully. Cook few seconds longer. Repeat.

SOUR CREAM PANCAKES

I received this recipe from Barbo Goldstein, which I modified slightly.

2 eggs, beaten
$^1/_3$ cup sour cream (75 mL)
$^1/_4$ cup Whey Bake Mix, (50 mL)
 page 68
2 tsp SPLENDA® Granular (10 mL)
1 tsp vanilla extract (5 mL)

Yield: 6 pancakes
1 pancake
64.4 calories
4.1 g g protein
4.3 g fat
1.9 g carbs

In medium bowl, beat eggs with fork. Add sour cream and beat again. Add Whey Bake Mix, page 68, SPLENDA® Granular and vanilla extract. Continue beating with fork until fairly smooth. Drop by approximately 3 tbsp (45 mL) onto hot, greased frying pan. Cook until browned on one side, flip and cook other side briefly.

Helpful Hint: Protein Bake Mix, page 68 is not suitable for this recipe.

HAM AND CHEESE QUICHE

I like to make my quiche with a crust, but you're welcome to omit it. This quiche is so good that you can serve it to non low-carbers, and they wouldn't guess!

Crust:
$^1/_2$ cup ground almonds (125 mL)
$^1/_3$ cup grated Parmesan cheese (75 mL)
2 tbsp soy, OR spelt flour (25 mL)
3 tbsp unsalted butter, melted (45 mL)
1 egg yolk
Filling:
$1^1/_2$ cups half-and-half cream (375 mL)
$1^1/_2$ cups cubed canned ham (375 mL)
2 tbsp green onion, chopped (25 mL)
3 eggs
$^1/_4$ tsp salt (1 mL)
$^1/_8$ tsp white pepper (0.5 mL)
1 cup grated Swiss or Mozzarella cheese (250 mL)
2 tbsp grated Parmesan Cheese (25 mL)

> **Yield:** 8 servings
> 1 serving
> 251.6 calories
> 17.0 g protein
> 18.6 g fat
> **4.9 g carbs**

Crust: In medium bowl, combine ground almonds, Parmesan cheese, soy or spelt flour, butter and egg yolk. Press into 9-inch (23 cm) glass pie dish. Bake in 350°F (180°C) oven 10 minutes.

Filling: In large bowl, combine half-and-half cream, ham and green onion. In small bowl, beat eggs, adding salt and pepper. Stir into cream mixture along with Swiss or Mozzarella cheese. Pour over crust. Sprinkle with Parmesan cheese. Bake 15 minutes at 400°F (200°C). Reduce heat to 325°F (160°C); bake 25 minutes more. Let stand 10 minutes before serving.

Variation: **Salmon Quiche:** Use 1 cup (250 mL) canned, deboned salmon, flaked, and add 1 tsp (5 mL) dried parsley. (*5.0 g Carbs*)

Helpful Hints: Without crust. (*2.9 g Carbs*) **75-80% Fat Fast:** 1 serving. (Replace half-and-half cream with whipping cream and omit crust.) (259.7 calories, 12.4 g protein, 22.5 g fat (77.5%), 2.3 g carbs)

~~Low-Carb Dieting Tip~~
Calories do count for most people, and especially as one gets closer to goal weight, when losing becomes more difficult.

DESSERT OMELET

Tired of a savory breakfast, but still want the egg to keep hunger at bay? This pancake-like omelet could be the answer.

1 egg
1 tsp whipping cream (5 mL)
1 tsp whey protein powder, OR soy flour,
 OR vital wheat gluten (5 mL)
1 tsp SPLENDA® Granular (5 mL)
$^1/_8$ tsp butter (0.5 mL)

Yield: 1 serving	
1 serving	
102.4 calories	
7.8 g protein	
7.1 g fat	
1.3 g carbs	

In cereal bowl, beat egg, whipping cream, whey protein powder, soy flour or vital wheat gluten and SPLENDA® Granular together with fork or whisk. Do not be concerned about any lumps. Melt butter in 6-inch (15 cm) nonstick frying pan and spread. Pour egg batter in. Cook until set, flip and cook briefly on other side. Serve with Crème Fraiche, page 70 and a sliced strawberry or a couple of raspberries, if desired, or spread with 1 tsp (5 mL) Splenda jam and top with dollop of Crème Fraiche, page 70. Fold and serve.

Variations: **Cream Cheese Dessert Omelet:** Add 0.5 oz (14 g) cream cheese. Sprinkle over uncooked egg in pan in tiny pieces. Cook and flip omelet. (*1.8 g Carbs*)

Savory Omelet: Omit SPLENDA® Granular. Add $^1/_8$ tsp (0.5 mL) salt. (*0.8 g Carbs*).

Savory Cheese Omelet: Add 0.5 oz (14 g) grated cheese to one half of omelet; fold over when set underneath. Continue cooking briefly until cheese melts. (*1.0 g Carbs*)

Helpful Hints: Dessert omelet using soy flour or vital wheat gluten. (*1.8 g Carbs*).

75-80% Fat Fast: Cream Cheese Dessert Omelet: 1 serving. (149.7 calories, 9.2 g protein, 11.6 g fat (70.3%), 1.8 g carbs)

~~Low-Carb Dieting Tip~~
Excess protein can be converted to glucose through glucogenesis, thereby raising insulin levels in the body.

CREATE-A-FLAVOR MOCK DANISH

The idea for this came from the Atkins' Friends' board. These are my variations, specifically useful for the Fat Fast. I wish I could tell you why it's called a Mock Danish – I can only guess at it!

2 oz regular cream cheese (60 g)
1 egg yolk
1 tbsp Da Vinci® Sugar Free (15 mL)
 syrup (any flavor)

> *Yield:* 1 serving
> 1 serving
> 248.4 calories
> 8.5 g protein
> 22.9 g fat (82.9%)
> *2.2 g carbs*

In cereal bowl, cover and nuke cream cheese 30 to 40 seconds, until softened. Add egg yolk and syrup. Whisk vigorously with wire whisk. Nuke 45 seconds for a runny center and 1 minute for a set result.

Variations: **75-80% Fat Fast:** 1 serving.
Chocolate Mock Danish: Use Da Vinci® Sugar Free Chocolate syrup and also $^1/_2$ tsp (2 mL) cocoa.
(250.1 calories, 8.6 g protein, 23.0 g fat (82.0%), 2.3 g carbs)

Peanut Butter Mock Danish: Add 2 tsp (10 mL) peanut butter.
(310.0 calories, 10.7 g protein, 28.1 g fat (81.4%), 3.7 g carbs)

Maple Walnut Mock Danish: Add 1 tbsp (15 mL) Da Vinci® Sugar-Free Pancake syrup (maple-flavored) and 1 tbsp (15 mL) finely chopped walnuts.
(295.9 calories, 10.4 g protein, 27.3 g fat (82.0%), 2.7 g carbs)

Chocolate Peanut Butter Delight: Omit egg yolk. Use 1 oz (30 g) cream cheese. Whisk in 1 tsp (5 mL) whipping cream, 1 tsp (5 mL) peanut butter, $^1/_2$ tsp (2 mL) cocoa and 1 tbsp (15 mL) Da Vinci® Sugar Free Chocolate syrup. If desired, sprinkle with grated unsweetened chocolate and 3 chopped pecans.
(141.9 calories, 4.2 g protein, 13.1 g fat (81.7%), 2.0 g carbs)

With 2 oz (60 g) cream cheese:
(236.4 calories, 7.7 g protein, 22.0 g fat (82.6%), 2.9 g carbs)

~~Low-Carb Dieting Tip~~
Count those carbohydrate grams and watch out for "hidden" carbs.

BREAKFAST BURRITO

This makes an excellent envelope for savory burrito ground beef (See Splendid Low-Carbing, page 52) or any other filling of your choice.

3 eggs, separated
1 tbsp whipping cream (15 mL)
2 tbsp Parmesan cheese (25 mL)
$^1/_2$ tsp dried parsley (2 mL)
$^1/_8$ tsp salt (0.5 mL)

Yield: 2 servings
1 serving
140.6 calories
12.0 g protein
9.4 g fat
1.2 g carbs

In medium bowl, beat egg whites until stiff, however, not dry. In small bowl, combine egg yolks and cream with fork. Fold into egg whites along with Parmesan cheese, parsley and salt.

Spray 9-inch (23 cm) glass pie dish with nonstick cooking spray. Pour egg mixture into pie dish. Microwave approximately 3 minutes, or until set.

Helpful Hint: Make sure there are no lumps in the Parmesan cheese.

PUFFY BAKED OMELET

A useful recipe to feed a crowd! This omelet served with spicy, chunky, salsa has a distinct Mexican flavor. Spicy Salsa has been scientifically proven to raise the metabolism, as does drinking ice cold water!

12 eggs
$^2/_3$ cup sour cream (150 mL)
2 tbsp whipping cream (25 mL)
2 tbsp water (25 mL)
1 tsp salt (5 mL)
$^1/_4$ cup chopped green onions (50 mL)
1 cup cheddar cheese (250 mL)
1 tsp Salsa, per serving (5mL)
  (optional)

Yield: 8 to 12 servings
1 serving
213.3/142.2 calories
13.8/9.2 g protein
16.4/10.9 g fat
2.1/1.5 g carbs

In blender, blend eggs, sour cream, whipping cream, water and salt. Liberally spray 9 x 13-inch (23 x 33 cm) glass baking dish with nonstick cooking spray. Pour omelet mixture into baking dish. Stir in green onions. Sprinkle cheese overall. Bake in 325°F (160°C) oven 30 minutes, or until set. Serve with Salsa, if desired.

NUTTY FRENCH TOAST

Another delicious recipe from Barbo Goldstein. Very filling!

2 oz light, OR regular
  cream cheese, softened (60 g)
3 eggs
$^1/_4$ cup Whey Bake Mix, (50 mL)
  page 68
2 tbsp SPLENDA® Granular (25 mL)
2 tsp vanilla extract (10 mL)
$^1/_4$ tsp cinnamon (1 mL)
$^1/_2$ tsp butter (2 mL)
2 tbsp chopped pecans or almonds (25 mL)

> *Yield:* 2 servings
> 1 serving
> 299.8 calories
> 17.0 g protein
> 21.3 g fat
> *7.5 g carbs*

In food processor or blender, process cream cheese and eggs. Add Whey Bake Mix, page 68, SPLENDA® Granular, vanilla extract and cinnamon; process.

Add butter to 8-inch (20 cm) nonstick frying pan. Add chopped pecans or almonds and cook until sizzling. Pour batter overall. Cook covered until it is setting well. Divide in quarters and flip each quarter. Cook other side briefly.

Helpful Hints: Barbo served this on top of warm ham steak and she used 2 tbsp (25 mL) Low-carb Maple Syrup for each serving, heated with a bit of butter in it, poured overall. Protein Bake Mix, page 68, is not suitable for this recipe.

Menu #7 75 to 80% Fat Fast	Calories	Protein	Fat	Carbs	%Fat
Chocolate Glazed Protein Bar, p. 87	222.0	9.0	19.0	4.6	73.0
Bacon Cheese Spread, SLC p. 25 with ½ cup (125 mL) cucumber	183.5	7.9	15.8	2.2	80.4
Vanilla Cream Jelly, p. 73	200.8	2.7	20.8	1.7	91.4
Scrambled Egg Bake	225.5	11.6	18.7	2.5	74.7
Deluxe White Choc., p. 90 with f.f. Cond. Milk (4 pieces)	147.2	4.4	13.6	2.4	81.6
TOTAL	**979.0**	**35.6**	**87.9**	**13.4**	**80.2**

BREAKFAST HASH

Delicious and different. Fried radishes lose that characteristic bite. A nice alternative to hash browns!

8 slices bacon, chopped
2 cups coarsely chopped red (500 mL)
  radishes, ends trimmed
$1/2$ cup chopped onion (125 mL)
$1/2$ tsp salt (2 mL)
$1/4$ tsp black pepper (1 mL)
$1/4$ tsp paprika (1 mL)
2 green onions, chopped

Yield: 4 servings
1 serving
104.5 calories
11.9 g protein
4.3 g fat
3.0 g carbs

In skillet or wok, fry bacon until some of the fat releases. Add radishes and onion. Sprinkle with salt, pepper and paprika. Stir-fry about 7 to 10 minutes, until radishes are tender. Add green onions during last 5 minutes of cooking.

Variation: **Deluxe Breakfast Hash:** Add 2 cups (500 mL) cubed, cooked chicken.

JUMBO RICOTTA PANCAKE

So quick and easy and absolutely delicious!

2 eggs
$1/4$ cup Ricotta cheese (50 mL)
1 tbsp SPLENDA® Granular (15 mL)
1 tsp vanilla extract (5 mL)

Yield: 1 serving
1 Jumbo Ricotta Pancake
228.7 calories
19.2 g protein
13.1 g fat
5.5 g carbs

In small bowl, beat eggs with fork. Whisk in ricotta cheese, SPLENDA® Granular and vanilla extract. Pour into 8-inch (20 cm) non-stick frying pan and as it begins to brown underneath, place lid over top. Cook until set on top, about 1 minute. Serve immediately with dollop of Crème Fraiche, page 70, if desired.

Helpful Hint: If desired, replace sweetener with 1 tbsp (15 mL) Da Vinci® Sugar Free Flavored syrup. (*4.5 g Carbs*)

MEAT

BEEF STEW

*Very tender beef in a delicious gravy. Instead of potatoes, there are water
chestnuts to add crunch and texture. Unusual, but really good!*

olive oil for frying
2 kg stewing beef (4.4 lbs)
seasoning salt to taste
2 cups whole water chestnuts (500 mL)
10 oz can sliced mushrooms (284 mL)
$^1/_2$ cup sliced onion (125 mL)
$^1/_3$ cup tomato paste (75 mL)
4 cloves garlic, crushed
2 tbsp instant beef stock mix (25 mL)
1 tbsp Worcestershire sauce (15 mL)
2 tsp soy sauce (10 mL)
2 tsp dried parsley flakes (10 mL)
1 tsp Thickening Agent, page 60 (5 mL)
$^1/_4$ tsp black pepper (1 mL)
4 cups water (1 L)

Yield: 10 servings
1 serving
350.5 calories
45.5 g protein
14.5 g fat
4.7 g carbs

In large nonstick frying pan, brown beef in batches in small amount of olive oil.
Sprinkle with seasoning salt. In large turkey roaster, place stewing beef and
juices from cooking, water chestnuts, mushrooms, onion, tomato paste, garlic,
instant beef stock mix, Worcestershire sauce, soy sauce, parsley flakes,
Thickening Agent, page 60 and black pepper. Stir in water. Cover roaster and
bake in 400°F (200°C) oven 30 minutes. Reduce heat to 350°F (180°C) and bake
an additional 2 hours, stirring occasionally.

Variation: **Curried Beef Stew:** Stir in 2 tbsp (25 mL) Curry Powder, page 61.

~~*Low-Carb Dieting Tip*~~
Increased hunger can be experienced just before a woosh. Resist!

CABBAGE ROLLS

I think you will agree that this recipe is delicious! You won't miss the rice!

2 lb lean ground beef or pork (0.9 kg)
$^1/_2$ cup crushed crisp breads, (125 mL)
  such as Wasa®
2 tbsp dehyrdated chopped onion (25 mL)
2 eggs
$1^1/_2$ tsp salt (7 mL)
$^1/_2$ tsp black pepper (2 mL)
$^1/_4$ tsp garlic powder (1 mL)
14 large cabbage leaves
Tomato-Chili Sauce:
14 oz can tomato sauce (284 mL)
$^3/_4$ cup water (175 mL)
$5^1/_2$ fl oz can tomato paste (156 mL)
2 tbsp SPLENDA® Granular (25 mL)
1 tsp dried basil (5 mL)
$^1/_2$ tsp chili powder (2 mL)
$^1/_4$ tsp salt (1 mL)

Yield: 14 servings
1 serving
176.0 calories
13.8 g protein
10.2 g fat
5.6 g carbs

In large bowl, combine ground beef, crushed crisp breads, onion, eggs, salt, pepper and garlic powder.

In large electric frying pan or large pot, with hot water, place 3 cabbage leaves at a time. Cover and allow to soften at least one minute. Remove to clean dinner plate. On another clean dinner plate, place one large cabbage leaf. Cut harder, stalky end off. Form some of meat mixture into small roll to fit cabbage leaf, fold in sides and roll up to form bundles; secure with wooden toothpicks as necessary. Place cabbage roll in 9 x 13-inch (23 x 33 cm) glass baking dish. Repeat with remaining meat and cabbage leaves.

Tomato-Chili Sauce: In blender combine tomato sauce, water, tomato paste, SPLENDA® Granular, basil, chili powder and salt. Pour over cabbage rolls. Cover with foil.

Bake in 375°F (190°C) oven 2 hours. Remove foil, baste cabbage rolls with sauce and bake another 20 minutes.

Helpful Hint: Normally, I assemble the cabbage rolls the night before, cover with foil and refrigerate. Then in the morning, I quickly blend the sauce, pour over cabbage rolls, cover with foil again and bake as directed.

LEMON LAMB ROAST

Lamb is extremely popular in India, South Africa, New Zealand, Australia and England, however, it is an acquired taste. This roast made my hubby very happy – so happy he went back for a third helping!!!

2 kg leg of lamb (4.4 lbs)
juice of 1 lemon
$1^1/_2$ tsp seasoning salt (7 mL)
1 tsp oregano (5 mL)
$^1/_4$ tsp black pepper (1 mL)
3 cloves garlic, slivered
1 cup hot water (250 mL)
2 tbsp butter (25 mL)
Gravy:
Pan scrapings
1 cup hot water (250 mL)
1 envelope instant beef stock mix (15 mL)
$^1/_2$ tsp Thickening Agent, page 60 (2 mL)
salt and pepper to taste

Yield: 8 servings
1 serving
337.0 calories
52.3 g protein
12.4 g fat
1.0 g carbs

Place leg of lamb in baking pan. Rub all over with juice of lemon. In small bowl, combine seasoning salt, oregano and black pepper. Sprinkle over lamb on both sides. Make small slits all over lamb and insert small slivers of garlic. Bake in 325°F (160°C) oven 30 minutes. Remove pan and add water, putting dabs of butter on top of leg. Roast another 3 to $3^1/_2$ hours, or until meat thermometer reads 175°F for medium or 180°F for well done. Baste roast occasionally with juices in pan. Once done, roast will be browned nicely.

Gravy: Remove roast. To scrapings in pan, add hot water and instant beef stock mix. Pour into small saucepan and sprinkle Thickening Agent, page 60 over gravy. Bring to boil. Add salt and pepper to taste.

Helpful Hints: Add vegetables of choice in last one hour of roasting and baste with juices in baking pan. Roasting times vary, however, typically for medium roast, lamb is roasted 20 to 25 minutes per lb (0.454 kg) or 25 to 30 minutes per lb (0.454 kg) for well done. Allow lamb to rest 20 minutes in turned off oven with door ajar before carving. Serve with gravy and/or traditional mint sauce. This gravy is not meant to be thick, however, if thicker gravy is preferred, add extra Thickening Agent.

CHEESE TACOS

You're in for a treat with these! Way tastier than corn tacos! See Helpful Hints below for an explanation regarding this recipe.

1 lb lean ground beef (0.454 kg)
1 cup water (250 mL)
10 Cheese Tacos (use 1.2 oz (34 g) grated
  Cheddar cheese per taco) – see below
$^2/_3$ cup shredded lettuce (150 mL)
2 large tomatoes, finely chopped
$^2/_3$ cup sour cream (150 mL)

Taco Mix:
2 tbsp dehydrated onion flakes (25 mL)
2 tsp ground cumin (10 mL)
$^3/_4$ tsp hot chili powder (3 mL)
$^1/_2$ tsp salt (2 mL)
$^1/_2$ tsp garlic powder (2 mL)
$^1/_8$ tsp Thickening Agent, page 60 (0.5 mL)

Yield: 10 servings
1 serving
363.7 calories
21.7 g protein
18.1 g fat
2.8 g carbs

In large frying pan, brown ground beef. Pour off fat. Stir Taco Mix into cooked ground beef, along with water. Bring to boil, reduce heat and simmer until sauce thickens and onion is soft.

Taco Mix: In small bowl, combine onion flakes, cumin, chili powder, salt, garlic powder, and Thickening Agent, page 60.

Cheese Tacos: Spread grated Cheddar cheese to cover surface in nonstick 6-inch (15 cm) pan. Melt until turning brown and it begins to bubble up, or until it flips easily (takes a while); flip, cook very briefly and fold over. Allow to cool briefly and fill with ground beef, lettuce, chopped tomato and sour cream.

Serve immediately with a Garden salad or Caesar salad on the side, if desired.

Variation: Taco Omelet: Taco Meat is a great filling for omelets.
Yield: 10 servings, or 50 g (1.8 oz) per serving. (*0.8 g Carbs*)

Helpful Hints: Unless you're feeding a crowd, you will not require 10 cheese tacos. One cheese taco with 50 grams (1.8 oz) taco beef, 1 tbsp (15 mL) shredded lettuce, 2 tbsp (25 mL) chopped tomato and 1 tbsp (15 mL) sour cream will yield the above nutritional analysis.

If tacos become too brittle to fill without breaking, warm in microwave oven 25 seconds and fill.

APPLE CURRY MEAT LOAF

The sweet taste of apple and "ketchup" contrasted with curry, makes this meat loaf really good.

1 1/2 lb lean ground beef (0.680 kg)
1 apple, peeled, cored and grated
1/4 cup wheat bran (50 mL)
2 tbsp dehydrated chopped onion (25 mL)
2 eggs
1 tbsp tomato paste (15 mL)
1 tbsp SPLENDA® Granular (15 mL)
1 tbsp curry powder (15 mL)
1 tsp Worcestershire sauce (5 mL)
3/4 tsp salt (3 mL)
1/2 tsp black pepper (2 mL)
Topping:
3 tbsp tomato paste (45 mL)
1 tbsp SPLENDA® Granular (15 mL)
1 tsp white vinegar (5 mL)

> *Yield:* 8 servings
> 1 serving
> 229.9 calories
> 18.3 g protein
> 14.4 g fat
> *5.3 g carbs*

In large bowl, combine ground beef, apple, wheat bran and onion. In small bowl, combine eggs, tomato paste, SPLENDA® Granular, curry powder, Worcestershire sauce, salt and pepper. Add to ground beef and mix well. Press mixture into 9 x 5 x 3-inch (2 L) loaf pan.

Topping: In small bowl, combine tomato paste, SPLENDA® Granular and vinegar. Cover meat loaf with topping. Bake in 350°F (180°C) oven 1 1/2 hours.

Variation: **Apple Meat Loaf:** Omit curry powder.

Menu #1 **85 to 90% Fat Fast**	Calories	Protein	Fat	Carbs	%Fat
Hot Chocolate, p. 5	190.6	2.3	19.5	2.5	85.5
Panna Cotta, p. 72	304.8	3.1	31.9	3.1	92.1
Broccoli Salad, SLC p. 32	134.7	2.0	13.3	2.1	85.3
Linda's Ice Cream Custard, p. 71	177.0	2.5	18.1	1.8	90.5
Quiche Lorraine, SLC p. 37	196.3	5.8	18.6	1.9	84.5
TOTAL	**1003.4**	**15.7**	**101.4**	**11.4**	**87.6**

TACO DOG
A simple meal, but very tasty!

1 Cheese Taco, page 33
1 6-inch hot dog, boiled
2 tbsp shredded lettuce (25 mL)
1 tbsp chopped tomato (15 mL)
2 tsp Salsa (10 mL)
2 tsp sour cream (10 mL)

Yield: 1 serving
1 Taco Dog
251.3 calories
13.2 g protein
20.1 g fat
4.3 g carbs

Prepare Cheese Taco, page 33. Insert hot dog, shredded lettuce, chopped tomato, Salsa and top with sour cream. Serve immediately.

Helpful Hints: If Cheese Taco becomes too brittle to open, microwave 25 seconds and fill. **75-80% Fat Fast:** 1 serving. (71.5% fat)

SPICY SLOPPY JOES
This is spicy, but you can easily turn down the heat by using less chili powder.

2 lb lean ground beef (0.9 kg)
10 oz can sliced mushrooms, (284 mL)
  undrained
5$^1/_2$ oz can tomato paste (156 mL)
$^1/_2$ cup water (125 mL)
4 cloves garlic, crushed
1 tbsp SPLENDA® Granular (15 mL)
1 tbsp vinegar (15 mL)
2 tsp salt (10 mL)
1 tsp hot chili powder (5 mL)
$^1/_4$ tsp black pepper (1 mL)

Yield: 8 servings
1 serving
270.9 calories
22.5 g protein
17.4 g fat
4.2 g carbs

In large electric frying pan, brown beef. Pour off fat. Stir in can mushrooms, tomato paste, water, garlic, SPLENDA® Granular, vinegar, salt, chili powder and black pepper. Bring to boil. Reduce heat and simmer until liquid reduces substantially.

Serve over low-carb bread or half low-carb hamburger bun or use as filling for Breakfast Burrito, page 27.

BAVARIAN CROCK-POT ROAST

Make sure you only have one quarter of an apple with your serving.

4 large apples, cored and
  quartered
$1^1/_2$ cups water (375 mL)
2 tsp SPLENDA® Granular (10 mL)
3 lbs Pork Loin Roast, OR (1.360 kg)
  Eye of Round Beef Roast
2 tsp olive oil (10 mL)
$1^1/_2$ tsp salt (7 mL)
1 tsp ground ginger (5 mL)
$^1/_4$ tsp white pepper (1 mL)
4 whole cloves
1 tsp Thickening Agent, page 60 (5 mL)
salt and pepper to taste

Yield: 6 servings
1 serving
434.3 calories
49.1 g protein
22.7 g fat
4.9 g carbs

Place the apples in bottom of crock-pot. Pour water and SPLENDA® Granular over apples. Place roast on top. Rub roast with oil. In small bowl, combine salt, ginger and pepper; rub over roast. Stick cloves in roast. Cook on high power 6 to 7 hours or on low power about 11 hours. Remove cloves. For gravy, in medium saucepan, place 2 cups (500 mL) remaining liquid. Sprinkle Thickening Agent, page 60 over top. Add salt and pepper to taste. Whisk and bring to boil.

SIRLOIN STEAK WITH LEMON PARSLEY

Too cold to barbecue outside? Enjoy your steak oven-broiled instead.

$2^1/_2$ lbs beef loin top sirloin (1.1 kg)
  steak (boneless)
1 tsp steak seasoning (5 mL)
Lemon Parsley Dressing:
3 tbsp olive oil (45 mL)
2 tbsp lemon juice (25 mL)
2 tbsp dried parsley (25 mL)
1 garlic clove, crushed
$^1/_4$ tsp salt (1 mL)
$^1/_8$ tsp black pepper (0.5 mL)

Yield: 6 servings
1 serving
412.6 calories
55.5 g protein
19.3 g fat
0.8 g carbs

Sprinkle steak on both sides with steak seasoning. Place on rack of broiling pan and broil steak about 5 minutes per side.

Lemon Parsley Dressing: In small bowl, combine olive oil, lemon juice, parsley, garlic, salt and pepper. Slice steak diagonally; sprinkle with dressing.

POULTRY

CHICKEN A LA QUEEN

This casserole, fit for a low-carb queen, looks and tastes delicious!

$^{1}/_{4}$ cup butter, divided (50 mL)
$^{1}/_{2}$ cup chopped onion (125 mL)
8 chicken breast halves, cut into
  bite size pieces
$^{1}/_{2}$ tsp salt (2 mL)
1, 10 oz can sliced mushrooms (284 mL)
$^{2}/_{3}$ cup half-and-half cream (150 mL)
2 oz light cream cheese pieces (60 g)
1 tbsp instant chicken stock mix (15 mL)
$^{1}/_{2}$ tsp Thickening Agent, page 60 (2 mL)
$^{1}/_{8}$ tsp white pepper (0.5 mL)
$^{1}/_{2}$ cup water (125 mL)
Biscuit Topping:
Savory Cheese Biscuits, page 63
  (use half-and-half cream)

Yield: 10 servings
1 serving
419.1 calories
44.6 g protein
24.3 g fat
5.4 g carbs

In electric frying pan or large skillet, melt half butter and stir-fry onion until browned. Set aside. In remaining butter, cook chicken (sprinkle with salt) until turning white. Add mushrooms, half-and-half cream, cream cheese, instant chicken stock mix, Thickening Agent, page 60 and white pepper. Bring to boil, reduce heat and simmer until sauce thickens. Stir in water and cooked onions.

Pour mixture into 9 x 13-inch (23 x 33 cm) glass baking dish. Cover with large dollops, about 3 tbsp (45 mL) Savory Cheese Biscuit dough, page 63 over entire casserole.

Bake in 350°F (180°C) oven 20 minutes, or until biscuit topping is golden brown.

~~Low-Carb Dieting Tip~~
Diet soft drinks containing aspartame, caffeine, sodium or citric acid may stall some people. If citric acid is not a problem, flavor carbonated water with Da Vinci® Gourmet Sugar Free Flavored syrup of choice.

BARBECUE CHICKEN PIZZA

These pizza crusts will puff up like a crispy, deep dish Italian pizza crust. Analysis for crust alone, (4.2 g Carbs).

Pizza Crust:

1 cup water, PLUS 2 tbsp (275 mL)
3 tbsp olive oil (45 mL)
2 large eggs
1¼ cups vital wheat gluten (300 mL)
1 cup whole wheat pastry flour (250 mL)
½ cup wheat bran (125 mL)
4 tsp bread machine yeast (20 mL)
1 tbsp SPLENDA® Granular (15 mL)
1 tbsp granulated sugar (15 mL)
1 tsp salt (5 mL)
1 tsp vanilla extract (5 mL)
3 tbsp olive oil (45 mL)

Topping: (all ingredients divided)

Barbecue Sauce, page 61
4 cups diced cooked Chicken (600 g)
6 slices cooked bacon, chopped
1 medium tomato, thinly sliced
¼ cup chopped green onion, OR (50 mL)
  green pepper
2½ cups Mozzarella or Cheddar cheese (625 mL)

Yield: 24 slices (2 pizzas)
1 slice
167.1 calories
16.2 g protein
8.6 g fat
5.3 g carbs

Pizza Crust: In cereal bowl, heat water in microwave oven 1 minute. In bread pan, place water, 3 tbsp (45 mL) olive oil, eggs, vital wheat gluten, whole wheat pastry flour, wheat bran, yeast, SPLENDA® Granular, sugar, salt and vanilla extract. Program bread machine to Pizza Dough setting or to knead and one rise. Remove and place on "floured" (use whey protein powder, vital wheat gluten or soy protein isolate) surface. Knead; divide dough in half. Roll out each half as much as possible. Cover with clean towel and leave 10 minutes. Roll again. If it resists rolling, let dough rest again. Grease two 12-inch (30 cm) pizza pans with butter. Lift each rolled-out pizza dough and place on pans. Roll out with small rolling pin, being careful to roll some of the thick edges back towards the center.

Bake in 450°F (230°C) oven 15 minutes. Brush underside of crusts with 3 tbsp (45 mL) olive oil.

Topping: Cover pizzas with Barbecue Sauce, page 61, and load up with warm chicken, bacon, tomato, green onion or green pepper and Mozzarella or Cheddar cheese. Bake 5 to10 minutes in 450°F (230°C) oven, or until cheese has melted.

JAMAICAN DRUMSTICKS

This is a lovely recipe from my friend, Sandra Van Harten, who often serves this at potluck lunches. Of course, she garnishes the platter so beautifully as well.

16 chicken drumsticks
Jerk Sauce:
1 cup crushed tomatoes (250 mL)
  (canned)
2 tbsp orange juice (25 mL)
2 tbsp SPLENDA® Granular, (25 mL)
  (optional)
2 tbsp olive oil (25 mL)
3 to 4 garlic cloves
2 green onions, chopped
$1/2$ jalapeno
$1/2$ shallot
$1/2$ –inch piece fresh ginger (1.5 cm)
1 tsp prepared mustard (5 mL)
1 tsp ground allspice (5 mL)
1 tsp salt (5 mL)
$1/4$ tsp white pepper (1 mL)

Yield: 16 drumsticks
1 drumstick
180.8 calories
26.6 g protein
6.7 g fat
1.8 g carbs

Drumsticks: Chop end of drumstick off with meat cleaver. A quick, hard, chop cuts it off. Push skin up and tuck in at top end with point of paring knife. What you wind up with is a very attractive looking finger food.

Jerk Sauce: In blender, combine tomatoes, orange juice, SPLENDA® Granular (if using), olive oil, garlic, green onions, jalapeno, shallot, ginger, mustard, allspice, salt and pepper. Blend until smooth. Spoon over chicken and, using hands, make sure each drumstick is well coated. Marinate overnight or at least 5 hours. Bake in 350°F (180°C) oven 1 hour. These may be served at room temperature or warm.

Helpful Hints: Do be careful to use a proper cutting surface and to practice extreme caution in cutting the drumsticks. Maybe enlist the help of someone who is strong. This operation may be omitted, if desired. Sandra likes to garnish the chicken drumsticks by placing them on a bed of lettuce or cabbage leaves with red and green pepper slivers on an attractive serving plate. The presentation looks stunning!

~~Low-Carb Dieting Tip~~
Glycerine in low-carb bars may stall some folks.

CROCK-POT CHICKEN DELIGHT

A hearty man's meal!!! This has become a regular meal in our household and is a particular favorite of my older son, Daniel.

3 tbsp butter (45 mL)
2¹/₂ lbs chicken breast halves (1.1 kg)
 (about 8)
3 pork sausages, diced
1 cup water (250 mL)
10 oz can sliced mushrooms, (284 mL)
 undrained
5¹/₂ fl oz can tomato paste (156 mL)
¹/₂ cup chopped onion (125 mL)
2 cloves garlic, crushed
1 tbsp paprika (15 mL)
1¹/₂ tsp salt (7 mL)
1 tsp ground ginger (5 mL)
¹/₂ tsp hot chili powder (2 mL)
¹/₂ cup whipping cream (125 mL)
³/₄ tsp Thickening Agent, page 60 (3 mL)

Yield: 8 servings
1 serving
264 calories
34.5 g protein
11.2 g fat
4.0 g carbs

In electric frying pan or large frying pan, melt butter. Add chicken breast halves and brown quickly on both sides. Cut chicken into small chunks. Add to crock-pot along with sausages. In medium bowl, stir together water, mushrooms, tomato paste, onion, garlic, paprika, salt, ginger and chili powder. Pour over meat. Stir to combine. Cover and cook on high setting 4 hours or on low setting 8 to 10 hours. Just before serving, switch off crock-pot and allow mixture to cool slightly. Stir in cream and Thickening Agent, page 60, until sauce thickens.

Serve over low-carb pasta, *Splendid Low-Carbing*, page 127, spaghetti squash, *Splendid Low-Carbing*, page 65 or zucchini pasta, *Splendid Low-Carbing*, page 53 if desired.

Helpful Hints: Use spaghetti pasta for non low-carbers in the family. I use Bavarian Smokies in this recipe, which imparts a lovely, smoked flavor.

~~Low-Carb Dieting Tip~~
Maltitol may stall some folks – check if it knocks you out of ketosis.

BALIHAI CHICKEN

Delicious hazelnut-crusted, curried chicken.

14 oz can coconut milk (398 mL)
1 tbsp SPLENDA® Granular (15 mL)
2 tsp soy sauce (10 mL)
2 tsp curry powder, page 61 (10 mL)
1 tsp salt (5 mL)
10 chicken breast halves (1 kg)
1 cup ground hazelnuts (250 mL)
¹⁄₃ cup olive oil (75 mL)

> **Yield:** 8 servings
> 1 serving
> 293.8 calories
> 35.4 g protein
> 15.6 g fat
> **2.1 g carbs**

In medium bowl, combine coconut milk, SPLENDA® Granular, soy sauce, curry powder, page 61 and salt. In 9 x 13-inch (23 x 33 cm) glass baking dish, place chicken and pour marinade over top. Marinate in refrigerator overnight.

Roll each chicken breast in ground hazelnuts. In electric frying pan or large frying pan, in hot oil, fry chicken 10 to 15 minutes, depending on thickness. Turn occasionally to brown evenly. Do not overcook chicken. Cook until chicken is no longer pink in center.

Helpful Hints: Fresh coconuts are often inexpensive. One gets a larger yield than in the cans. It's my husband's job to retrieve the coconut milk. Drill a hole in one side of coconut. Place over container and drill another "breathing" hole to allow the liquid to drain faster. Crack open shell with an axe. Scoop out white flesh, being careful not to get bits of shell. Blend liquid and white flesh together. Boil in double boiler to sterilize. Refrigerate in glass milk jug. See Coconut Chocolate Mousse, page 69 for a delightful dessert using leftover coconut milk.

Menu #2 **85 to 90% Fat Fast**	Calories	Protein	Fat	Carbs	%Fat
Vanilla Cream Jelly, p. 73	200.8	2.7	20.8	1.7	91.4
Crème Caramel Custard, p. 72	211.6	3.7	21.1	2.2	89.0
Zesty Veggie Dip, p. 11 with ½ cup (125 mL) cucumber	189.1	2.4	19.1	3.1	91.0
Blender Coconut Custard Pie, p.72	264.2	4.1	26.2	2.1	88.1
Strawberry Milk Shake, SLC p. 16	135.0	1.9	12.8	2.5	85.5
TOTAL	**1000.7**	**14.8**	**100.0**	**11.6**	**89.0**

GINGERED CHICKEN AND VEGETABLES

Colorful Chinese-style dinner.

6 chicken breast halves
$^1/_2$ tsp salt (0.5 mL)
$^1/_4$ tsp white pepper (1 mL)
$^1/_3$ cup soy sauce (75 mL)
3 tbsp water (45 mL)
1 tsp SPLENDA® Granular (5 mL)
$^1/_2$ tsp Thickening Agent, page 60 (2 mL)
$^1/_4$ cup olive oil, divided (50 mL)
2 tbsp finely chopped fresh ginger (25 mL)
$1^1/_2$ cups snow peas (375 mL)
1 red pepper, cut into thin strips

Yield: 6 servings	
1 serving	
244.8 calories	
33.0 g protein	
9.3 g fat	
4.8 g carbs	

Cut chicken breasts in half. Slice thin strips. Sprinkle with mixture of salt and pepper. Set aside. In small bowl, combine soy sauce, water, SPLENDA® Granular and Thickening Agent, page 60. Stir with wire whisk.

In wok or large electric frying pan, in 2 tbsp (25 mL) hot oil, cook ginger until turning brown. Add chicken and stir-fry until white with no pink showing inside. Set aside in colander to drain. In remaining oil, cook snow peas and red pepper 2 minutes, until tender crisp. Add chicken and sauce, stirring briefly until thickened.

Variation: Use sirloin tip steak strips instead, if desired.

~~Low-Carb Dieting Tip~~
Alcohol can make it difficult to lose weight by increasing carbohydrate cravings significantly in some folks.

CHICKEN CURRY

Excellent curry. Serve on Cauli-Fried Rice, page 53, if desired.

8 chicken breast halves, cut into
  bite-size pieces
$^1/_4$ cup olive oil (50 mL)
1 tsp salt (5 mL)
$^1/_4$ tsp black pepper (1 mL)
2 garlic cloves, crushed
2 tbsp olive oil (25 mL)
$^1/_2$ cup chopped onion (125 mL)
1 green pepper, chopped
$^1/_2$ cup chopped green onion (125 mL)
$^1/_4$ cup tomato paste (50 mL)
1 tbsp Curry Powder, page 61 (15 mL)
1 tbsp soy, OR vital wheat gluten (15 mL)
2 tsp dried parsley (10 mL)
1 cup water (125 mL)
2 tbsp seedless raisins (25 mL)
1 envelope chicken bouillon (15 mL)
$^1/_4$ cup slivered almonds, (50 mL)
  (optional)

Yield: 8 servings
1 serving
271.3 calories
31.6 g protein
12.6 g fat
6.0 g carbs

In wok or electric frying pan, heat $^1/_4$ cup (50 mL) olive oil and stir-fry chicken until turning white. Sprinkle chicken with salt and pepper and add garlic. Stir-fry a little longer. Set aside.

In 2 tbsp (25 mL) olive oil, stir-fry onion until soft. Add green pepper and green onion; stir-fry 2 minutes. Stir in tomato paste, Curry Powder, page 61, soy or vital wheat gluten flour and parsley. Add chicken. Stir in water, raisins and chicken bouillon. Stir until sauce begins to thicken, reduce heat and simmer 15 minutes. Add almonds in last 5 minutes, if using.

Serve with Microwave Peach Chutney, *Splendid Low-Carbing*, page 102 and a sprinkle of unsweetened coconut, if desired. This is delicious on Cauli-fried Rice, page 53.

~~Low-Carb Dieting Tip~~
Some medications can interfere with weight loss, including HRT.

CHINESE LEMON CHICKEN

Lovely light, crispy, battered chicken smothered in lemon sauce. Delicious!

1 extra-large egg
1 tsp water (5 mL)
$^1/_2$ tsp salt (2 mL)
$^1/_4$ tsp black pepper (1 mL)
2 tbsp vital wheat gluten (25 mL)
2 tbsp whey protein powder (25 mL)
  (natural)
$^1/_2$ tsp baking soda (2 mL)
$^1/_4$ tsp paprika (1 mL)
$^1/_8$ tsp salt (0.5 mL)
$^1/_8$ tsp cayenne pepper (0.5 mL)
4 boneless, skinless chicken breast halves
Lemon Sauce:
$^1/_3$ cup water (75 mL)
2 tbsp lemon juice (25 mL)
$^1/_3$ cup SPLENDA® Granular (75 mL)
$1^1/_2$ tsp instant chicken stock mix (7 mL)
1 tsp grated lemon peel (5 mL)
$^1/_2$ tsp butter (2 mL)
$^1/_2$ tsp Thickening Agent, page 60 (2 mL)

Yield: 4 servings
1 serving
185.3 calories
34.0 g protein
3.0 g fat
3.9 g carbs

In small bowl, beat egg, water, $^1/_2$ tsp (2 mL) salt and pepper together. In another small bowl, combine vital wheat gluten, whey protein powder, baking soda, paprika, salt and cayenne pepper. Spread this mixture out on dinner plate.

Dip each chicken breast half in egg wash and then roll in dry mixture. Place chicken on greased cookie sheet. Spray with nonstick cooking spray until surface looks moist. Bake chicken in 450°F (230°C) oven 20 minutes, or until no longer pink inside. Slice chicken crosswise into thin slices and pour Lemon Sauce over chicken. Serve immediately.

Lemon Sauce: In small saucepan, combine water, lemon juice, SPLENDA® Granular, instant chicken stock mix, lemon peel and butter. Sprinkle Thickening Agent, page 60 over warm sauce. Whisk and bring to boil.

~~Low-Carb Dieting Tip~~
To lose water weight, reduce sodium intake and drink lots of water.

FISH AND SHELLFISH

SWEET AND SOUR SHRIMP

A lovely sweet and sour sauce and tender crisp vegetables with large shrimp.

1 lb raw jumbo shrimp (0.454 kg)
1 tbsp olive oil (15 mL)
2 tbsp chopped fresh ginger (25 mL)
$^3/_4$ cup water (175 mL)
$^1/_4$ cup lemon juice (50 mL)
$^1/_4$ cup SPLENDA® Granular (50 mL)
$2^1/_2$ tbsp soy sauce (32 mL)
1 tsp Thickening Agent, page 60 (5 mL)
7.6 fl. oz sliced water chestnuts (227 mL)
  (canned)
1 green pepper, cut into chunks

Yield: 5 servings
1 serving
157.4 calories
19.2 g protein
4.5 g fat
7.4 g carbs

Prepare shrimp by removing shell, tails and veins (sometimes already removed). Set aside. In electric frying pan or wok, heat oil and add ginger. Stir-fry until turning brown.

Meanwhile in small bowl, combine water, lemon juice, SPLENDA® Granular and soy sauce. Add to frying pan. Sprinkle Thickening Agent, page 60 over warm sauce and bring to boil. Add shrimp and stir-fry 3 minutes. Add water chestnuts and green pepper and cook until heated through, about 2 more minutes. Serve over Cauli-fried Rice, page 53.

~~Low-Carb Dieting Tip~~
The closer you are to goal weight, the more difficult it is to lose weight. Exercise can really help keep things moving in the right direction.

SHRIMP CURRY

Super quick, super easy and super delicious. Good protein source.

3 tbsp Healthy butter, page 62 (45 mL)
2 cloves garlic, crushed
1 green pepper, chopped
24 oz frozen salad shrimp, (680 g)
  thawed
1 tbsp SPLENDA® Granular (15 mL)
$1^{1}/_{2}$ tsp curry powder (7 mL)
$^{1}/_{2}$ tsp Thickening Agent, page 60 (2 mL)
$^{1}/_{4}$ tsp seasoning salt (1 mL)
$^{1}/_{4}$ cup water (50 mL)
2 tbsp whipping cream (25 mL)

Yield: 4 servings
1 serving
320.6 calories
35.4 g protein
17.0 g fat
4.8 g carbs

In large electric frying pan, melt butter, add garlic and stir-fry until turning brown. Add green pepper and stir-fry 2 minutes. Add shrimp; cook 2 minutes. In small bowl, combine SPLENDA® Granular, curry powder, Thickening Agent, page 60 and seasoning salt. Sprinkle seasoning over shrimp and peppers. Stir in water and whipping cream and cook until sauce is slightly thickened, about 1 minute, or until shrimp are heated through.

Helpful Hints: This is wonderful served over Cauli-fried Rice, page 53. To thaw frozen shrimp: Rinse shrimp in colander over basin under cold running water 5 minutes. Shrimp curry is also delicious served in an omelet.

~~Low-Carb Dieting Tip~~
Glycogen stores will quickly be replenished after a carb binge. Glycogen stores water. Go back to induction levels for a couple of days to get rid of the water weight as well as the inevitable carb cravings.

TUNA PIE WITH YOGURT SAUCE
Excellent pie - even for company!

$^3/_4$ cup plain yogurt (175 mL)
$^1/_2$ cup mayonnaise (125 mL)
$^1/_4$ cup sour cream (50 mL)
$^1/_4$ cup chopped green onion (50 mL)
2 tbsp Worcestershire Sauce (25 mL)
1 tbsp SPLENDA® Granular (15 mL)
$^1/_2$ tsp dry mustard (2 mL)
$^1/_2$ tsp salt (2 mL)
$^1/_4$ tsp white pepper (1 mL)
$^1/_4$ tsp Tabasco Sauce (1 mL)
$1^1/_2$ lbs canned tuna, flaked (750 g)
3 extra-large eggs, fork beaten
$^1/_2$ cup oat bran (125 mL)
Yogurt Sauce:
1 cup yogurt (250 mL)
$^1/_2$ cup sour cream (125 mL)
2 tbsp white vinegar (25 mL)
2 tsp prepared mustard (10 mL)
1 tsp SPLENDA® Granular (5 mL)
$^1/_2$ tsp dried parsley (2 mL)
$^1/_4$ tsp salt (1 mL)
$^1/_8$ tsp white pepper (0.5 mL)

Yield: 12 servings
1 serving
224.8 calories
22.9 g protein
12.5 g fat
4.5 g carbs

In medium bowl, combine yogurt, mayonnaise, sour cream, green onion, Worcestershire Sauce, SPLENDA® Granular, mustard, salt, white pepper and Tabasco Sauce. In large bowl, combine tuna, eggs, oat bran and yogurt mixture. Press into 9 x 13-inch (23 x 33 cm) glass baking dish. Bake in 350°F (180°C) oven 35 to 40 minutes.

Yogurt Sauce: In medium bowl, combine yogurt, sour cream, vinegar, mustard, SPLENDA® Granular, parsley, salt and pepper. Refrigerate.

Serve tuna pie with Yogurt Sauce.

~~Low-Carb Dieting Tip~~
Make sure you consume iodized salt to maintain healthy thyroid function and avoid developing a goiter.

SALMON WITH FRUIT SALSA

Excellent, very tasty and super easy!

*8 salmon steaks,
{about 3 lbs (1.36 kg)}
2 tbsp lemon juice (25 mL)
Fruit Salsa:
1 orange, peeled, seeded and chopped
1 large tomato, chopped finely
$^1/_2$ cup chopped cucumber (125 mL)
$^1/_4$ cup chopped canned peaches, (50 mL)
  in juice, drained
3 tbsp chopped green onion (45 mL)
2 tbsp chopped jalapeno peppers (25 mL)
2 tbsp red wine vinegar (25 mL)
1 tbsp olive oil (15 mL)
1 tbsp SPLENDA® Granular (15 mL)
$^1/_2$ tsp seasoned salt (2 mL)
$^1/_4$ tsp garlic powder (1 mL)

> ***Yield:*** 8 servings
> 1 serving
> 276.9 calories
> 41.5 g protein
> 10.8 g fat
> ***3.4 g carbs***

Prepare fruit salsa earlier in day and refrigerate. Brush salmon steaks with lemon juice. Grill or broil salmon 6-inches (15 cm) from heat, 5 minutes on both sides, or until fish flakes easily with fork. Do watch carefully when last side is cooking, to prevent burning. Set timer for each side.

Fruit Salsa: In medium bowl, combine orange, tomato, cucumber, peaches, green onion, jalapeno peppers, red wine vinegar, olive oil, SPLENDA® Granular, seasoned salt and garlic powder. Refrigerate until needed. Serve salmon steaks with chilled Fruit Salsa spooned over each one.

*Helpful Hint: If only serving 2 to 4 people, use 4 salmon steaks and halve Fruit Salsa recipe.

~~Low-Carb Dieting Tip~~
MSG can trigger carbohydrate cravings.

CRAB CAKES
Great low-carb fare!

1 lb canned crab meat, (0.454 kg)
  picked over
2 green onions, chopped
$^1/_4$ cup red pepper, chopped (50 mL)
$^1/_4$ cup mayonnaise, page 58 (50 mL)
$^1/_4$ cup Ultimate Bake Mix, (50 mL)
  page 67
1 egg, fork beaten
2 tsp dried parsley (10 mL)
1 tsp seasoning salt (5 mL)
$^1/_2$ tsp dry mustard (2 mL)
$^1/_4$ tsp Worcestershire sauce (1 mL)
3 tbsp Healthy Butter, page 62 (45 mL)

Yield: 10 Crab Cakes
1 Crab Cake
104.8 calories
10.9 g protein
6.0 g fat
1.4 g carbs

In large bowl, combine crab meat, green onions, red pepper, mayonnaise, Ultimate Bake Mix, page 67, egg, parsley, seasoning salt, mustard and Worcestershire sauce. In large skillet or electric frying pan, melt some Healthy Butter, page 62. Using ice cream scoop, form mixture into balls and turn out onto hot skillet. Flatten crab cakes and cook until browned on both sides. Repeat with remaining mixture.

Helpful Hints: These are great with Mayonnaise, page 58 or Thousand Island Dressing, *Splendid Low-Carbing*, page 100. Crab cakes are delicate, so turn carefully.

75-80% Fat Fast: 1 crab cake and 1 tbsp (15 mL) Mayonnaise, page 58. (201.2 calories, 11.2 g protein, 16.6 g fat (73.7%), 1.9 g carbs)

~~Low-Carb Dieting Tip~~
Eat more fiber. Good sources of fiber are wheat bran, unsweetened dessicated coconut and pysillium husks.

SCALLOPS IN GARLIC CHEESE SAUCE

Absolutely decadent served over Cheese Biscuit halves, page 63.

6 slices bacon, chopped
2 green onions, chopped
2 cloves garlic, crushed
1 lb mushrooms, sliced (454 grams)
1.2 lb bay scallops (544 grams)
$^1/_4$ tsp Thickening Agent, page 60 (1 mL)
Cheese Sauce:
$^1/_2$ tsp dry mustard (2 mL)
$^1/_4$ tsp xanthan or guar gum (1 mL)
$^1/_4$ tsp salt (1 mL)
$^1/_4$ tsp white pepper (1 mL)
$^1/_2$ cup whipping cream (125 mL)
$^1/_4$ cup water (50 mL)
2 egg yolks, fork beaten
$1^1/_2$ cups grated Cheddar cheese (375 mL)

Yield: 6 servings
1 serving
344.0 calories
31.2 g protein
21.0 g fat
6.6 g carbs

In electric frying pan, fry bacon until crisp. Pour off most of bacon fat. Add green onions and garlic. Stir-fry briefly. Add mushrooms. Cook until mushrooms are soft and browned. Meanwhile prepare cheese sauce.

Cheese Sauce: In small nonstick saucepan, stir together dry mustard, xanthan gum, salt and white pepper. In small bowl, combine whipping cream and water. Gradually add whipping cream mixture to saucepan, stirring with whisk. Bring mixture to boil. Remove saucepan from heat. Add small amount of mixture to egg yolks; return to saucepan. Stir in 1 cup (250 mL) Cheddar cheese. Cook over very low heat until cheese melts. Do not boil. Remove from heat, if necessary.

Stir cheese sauce and scallops into mushroom mixture. Turn heat lower, cover and cook 5 minutes. Sprinkle with Thickening Agent, page 60 and boil 1 minute. Sprinkle with remaining cheese. Serve immediately over Cheese biscuit halves.

~~Low-Carb Dieting Tip~~
Cut Ketostix in half to save money.

SALMON ALMONDINE

Fresh salmon is considered one of the great fish delicacies of the world. So healthy, so delicious – great company fare too!

1 egg
1 clove garlic, finely chopped
1 tsp lime juice (5 mL)
$^1/_2$ tsp salt (2 mL)
$^1/_2$ tsp ground cumin (2 mL)
$^1/_4$ tsp black pepper (1 mL)
$^1/_2$ cup olive oil (125 mL)
2 tsp dried parsley, OR (10 mL)
4 sprigs chopped fresh parsley
2 lbs fresh salmon (0.9 kg)
2 tsp olive oil (10 mL)
$^1/_2$ cup sliced almonds, with skins on (125 mL)

Yield: 6 servings. 1 serving 479.4 calories 40.1 g protein 35.4 g fat ***1.4 g carbs***

In blender, place egg, garlic, lime juice, salt, cumin and pepper; blend. Through opening in lid of blender, very slowly pour $^1/_2$ cup (125 mL) olive oil, while operating blender at low speed. When thickened, stir in dried or fresh parsley. Place salmon in long baking dish. Brush 2 tsp (10 mL) olive oil over salmon. Spread sauce mixture over salmon and garnish with almonds.

Bake in 375°F (190°C) oven 30 minutes, or until salmon is barely firm.

~~Low-Carb Dieting Tip~~

To check if your thyroid is sluggish, take your temperature orally 4x a day, before each of your 3 meals and before you go to bed, for 4 days. If your average temperature each day is consistently below 98°F, schedule a medical check-up, as you may be suffering from some degree of hypothyroidism. The new guidelines narrow the range for acceptable thyroid stimulating hormone (TSH) to between 0.3 and 3.04 uU/ml. A good place to look on the internet is on the American Endocrinology Association's site and also the British Medical Journal's site. An important test to have done is a Thyroid antibody test, as this will often highlight a problem (as in Hashimoto's Thyroiditis) long before it shows up as dramatic changes in your TSH, T4 or T3 levels. In this case, your body is slowly destroying your thyroid. Prescription Thyroid hormone helps delay this inevitable process, also preventing or perhaps shrinking an existing goiter or enlargement of the gland.

CRAB STUFFED COD

My hubby thought these were nice and he is not a huge fish fan.

$1\frac{1}{2}$ lbs Cod, OR Sole fillets, OR (680 g)
  any white fish fillets
3 cans crab meat, (each 120 g)
  picked over
$\frac{1}{4}$ cup chopped green onions (50 mL)
$\frac{1}{4}$ cup Mayonnaise, page 58 (50 mL)
$\frac{1}{4}$ cup Parmesan cheese (50 mL)
1 egg
1 tbsp oat bran (15 mL)
$\frac{1}{2}$ tsp dry mustard (2 mL)
$\frac{1}{2}$ tsp Italian seasoning (2 mL)
$\frac{1}{4}$ tsp garlic powder (1 mL)
$\frac{1}{4}$ tsp paprika (1 mL)
$\frac{1}{4}$ tsp Tabasco sauce (1 mL)
$\frac{1}{8}$ tsp white pepper (0.5 mL)
$\frac{1}{4}$ cup Parmesan cheese (50 mL)

Yield: 8 servings
1 serving
212.2 calories
29.0 g protein
9.5 g fat
1.2 g carbs

Rinse and pat sole fillets dry with paper towels. Set aside. In medium bowl, combine crab meat, green onions, Mayonnaise, page 58, $\frac{1}{4}$ cup (50 mL) Parmesan Cheese, egg, oat bran, mustard, Italian seasoning, garlic powder, paprika, Tabasco sauce and white pepper. Place some crabmeat on each fillet and roll up. Secure with toothpicks. Place fillets in a glass baking dish. Sprinkle remaining crab stuffing over all.

Bake in 375°F (190°C) oven 30 minutes, or until fish flakes easily. Sprinkle with $\frac{1}{4}$ cup (50 mL) Parmesan cheese 10 minutes before end of baking time.

~~Low-Carb Dieting Tip~~

Keeping a food diary is helpful to identify stumbling blocks. Record daily weights to study the reasons for weight lost on certain days. Study your reaction to lower or higher calories, lower or higher carbohydrates, lower or higher protein, lower or higher fat over many months. Change one thing and stick to it for a couple of weeks to a month and then judge.

VEGETABLES

CAULI-FRIED RICE

This is my version of Chinese-fried rice using grated cauliflower. The color resembles golden brown rice. The cauliflower becomes denatured and hardly recognizable. It's delicious, especially freshly made.

$^1/_4$ cup Healthy Butter, page 62, (50 mL)
2 cloves garlic, crushed
1 green onion, chopped
6 cups cauliflower florets, (1.5 L)
  grated (about 1 medium head cauliflower)
2 tbsp soy sauce (25 mL)
$^1/_2$ tsp seasoning salt (2 mL)
2 eggs, fork beaten

Yield: 6 servings
1 serving
121.7 calories
4.4 g protein
9.6 g fat
4.3 g carbs

In electric frying pan or wok, melt Healthy Butter, page 62. Add garlic and green onion. Cook briefly. Add grated cauliflower and stir-fry 2 minutes. Stir in soy sauce and sprinkle seasoning salt overall. Stir-fry another 3 minutes; push aside. Add eggs and scramble in one corner of pan. Stir into cauli-rice another minute, or until cauli-rice is tender.

Variation: Add small pieces cooked chicken or pork to cauli-rice.

Helpful Hint: Food processor grates cauliflower in no time flat!

~~Low-Carb Dieting Tip~~
Exercise, exercise, exercise – have you exercised today?

MUSHROOM MOZZARELLA BAKE
Very tasty, scalloped mushrooms!

1 lb fresh mushrooms, sliced (0.454 kg)
3 tbsp Healthy Butter, page 62 (45 mL)
2 tbsp whipping cream (25 mL)
1 tsp seasoning salt (5 mL)
1 tsp dried parsley (5 mL)
$^1/_4$ tsp black pepper (1 mL)
$^3/_4$ cup grated Mozzarella cheese (175 mL)

Yield: 6 servngs
1 serving
127.3 calories
4.6 g protein
11.0 g fat
3.1 g carbs

In large frying pan or electric frying pan, fry mushrooms in Healthy Butter, page 62 until softening. Add whipping cream, seasoning salt, parsley and black pepper. Allow to simmer until whipping cream reduces slightly. Arrange mushrooms in shallow casserole dish. Sprinkle with cheese. Bake in 350°F (180°C) oven 10 minutes, or until cheese is melted.

Helpful Hint: **75-80% Fat Fast:** 1 serving (as an accompaniment). (74.0% fat)

ZUCCHINI TOMATO BAKE
Surprisingly delicious!

2 zucchini
1 large tomato, cut into chunks
$^1/_2$ cup chopped onion (125 mL)
1 tsp minced garlic (5 mL)
1 tsp basil (5 mL)
$^1/_2$ tsp salt (2 mL)
$^1/_4$ tsp black pepper (1 mL)
3 tbsp olive oil (45 mL)
$^1/_4$ cup grated Parmesan cheese (50 mL)

Yield: 4 servings.
1 serving
144.0 calories
4.0 g protein
12.3 g fat
3.9 g carbs

Slice zucchini in half and then cut into thin slices. In large bowl, combine zucchini, tomato, onion, garlic, basil, salt and pepper. Set aside 5 minutes. Stir in olive oil. Place in casserole dish with lid. Bake in 450°F (230°C) oven 20 minutes. Remove and drain slightly. Sprinkle with Parmesan cheese and replace lid. Reduce heat to 375°F (190°C) and bake another 20 minutes.

Helpful Hint: **75-80% Fat Fast:** 1 serving (as an accompaniment). (73.6% fat)

OVEN ZUCCHINI FRIES

These are delicious, slightly crispy on the outside and soft inside.

2 medium zucchini
2 tbsp olive oil (25 mL)
1 tbsp water (15 mL)
3 tbsp ground almonds (45 mL)
2 tbsp grated Parmesan cheese (25 mL)
$^1/_4$ tsp paprika (1 mL)
$^1/_4$ tsp salt (1 mL)
$^1/_8$ tsp black pepper (0.5 mL)
$^1/_8$ tsp garlic powder (0.5 mL)

Yield: 3 servings
1 serving
129.4 calories
4.4 g protein
11.1 g fat
2.8 g carbs

Slice zucchini in half lengthwise. Slice each half in quarters lengthwise and cut those quarters in half. Place olive oil and water in plastic bag. Add zucchini, seal bag and shake to moisten. In small bowl, combine ground almonds, Parmesan cheese, paprika, salt, black pepper and garlic powder. Dredge zucchini fries with almond mixture. Place in single layer on well-greased cookie sheet. Bake in 475°F (250°C) oven 12 to 17 minutes, or until golden brown. Be careful not to burn them.

Helpful Hint: **75-80% Fat Fast:** 1 serving. (73.6% fat)

CREAMED FAUX MASHED POTATOES

Honestly, I prefer this to mashed potatoes.

$1^1/_2$ lbs raw cauliflower (680 g)
3 oz regular cream cheese, (90 g)
  softened
2 tbsp whipping cream (25 mL)
1 tbsp butter (15 mL)
$^1/_2$ tsp salt (2 mL)
$^1/_4$ tsp white pepper (1 mL)

Yield: 8 servings
1 serving
80.9 calories
2.8 g protein
6.1 g fat
3.4 g carbs

Steam cauliflower 25 minutes, or until soft. In food processor, combine cauliflower, cream cheese, whipping cream, butter, salt and pepper. Process until smooth and thickened. Add 1 tbsp (15 mL) extra cream or water, if necessary.

ZUCCHINI FRITTERS

The idea for this recipe came from an Australian lady whose mother used to make something similar during rationing in the 2nd World War, although she used grated potato and called the fritters "Mock Fish".

$2^1/_4$ cups grated zucchini (550 mL)
2 cups grated Cheddar cheese (500 mL)
$^1/_4$ cup Ultimate Bake Mix, page 67 (50 mL)
2 tbsp dehydrated onion (25 mL)
2 cloves garlic, crushed
1 tsp instant chicken stock mix (5 mL)
$^1/_8$ tsp black pepper (0.5 mL)
2 well-beaten eggs
2 tbsp olive oil (25 mL)

Yield: 18 small fritters
1 fritter
70.7 calories
4.6 g protein
5.3 g fat
1.0 g carbs

In large bowl, combine zucchini, Cheddar cheese, Ultimate Bake Mix, page 67, dehydrated onion, garlic, chicken stock mix and black pepper. Stir in eggs. In frying pan, in some hot oil, fry several soup spoonfuls of mixture, flipping when crispy. Cook until crispy on other side as well.

Helpful Hint: Double the recipe and use an ice cream scoop for making the right size fritters. ***Yield:*** 22 large fritters. (***2.0 g Carbs***)

PEPPER CHUNKS AND STEWED TOMATO

I really like this vegetable combo.

2 tbsp Healthy Butter, page 62 (25 mL)
1 green pepper, cut into large chunks
3 medium tomatoes, peeled
1 tsp dried basil (5 mL)
$^1/_2$ tsp seasoning salt (2 mL)
$^1/_4$ tsp garlic powder (1 mL)
2 tbsp Parmesan cheese, (25 mL)
  (optional)

Yield: 6 servings
1 serving
60.6 calories
1.0 g protein
4.1 g fat
4.7 g carbs

In large frying pan, in Healthy Butter, page 62, stir-fry green pepper briefly, cover and cook about 10 minutes, until tender (stir occasionally). Cut tomatoes into chunks. Add to green pepper, together with basil, seasoning salt and garlic powder. Cover and simmer about 10 minutes. Sprinkle with Parmesan cheese.

Variation: **Stewed Tomatoes:** Omit green pepper and cook tomato about 10 minutes at higher heat, stirring occasionally. ***Yield:*** 4 servings. (***3.4 g Carbs***)

DELUXE GREEN BEANS ALMONDINE
A wonderful method to ensure these turn out just perfect each time!

1 lb fresh green beans (0.454 kg)
3 tbsp butter (45 mL)
2 cloves garlic, crushed
$^1/_4$ tsp salt (1 mL)
$^1/_3$ cup slivered almonds, (75 mL)
   toasted

Yield: 6 servings
1 serving
75.8 calories
1.5 g protein
5.9 g fat
4.3 g carbs

Cut green bean ends off, where necessary, and cut in half. Rinse in colander. Bring water (enough to cover beans) in large saucepan to boil, add beans and bring to boil again. Pour beans into colander and rinse with very cold water. This blanching of the green beans may be done earlier in the day.

In large electric frying pan or skillet, melt butter and add garlic. Stir-fry garlic briefly until just beginning to turn color. Add beans. Sprinkle with salt and stir-fry 10 minutes, or until tender-crisp. Add toasted almonds. Stir-fry briefly.

Helpful Hint: To toast almonds, add to dry nonstick frying pan on medium heat. Stir-fry until slightly brown.

FRIED MARINATED ONIONS
Different!

2 large onions
$^1/_4$ cup white vinegar (50 mL)
2 tbsp SPLENDA® Granular (25 mL)
2 tbsp mayonnaise (25 mL)
1 tsp dried parsley (5 mL)
1 tbsp soy, OR spelt flour (15 mL)
3 tbsp butter (45 mL)

Yield: 6 servings
$^1/_3$ cup (75 mL) per serving
73.9 calories
1.2 g protein
5.5 g fat
4.8 g carbs

Chop onions coarsely. In medium bowl, combine vinegar, SPLENDA® Granular, mayonnaise and parsley. Stir in onion. Refrigerate overnight. Drain onions. Stir in soy or spelt flour.

Melt butter in frying pan. Add onions and stir-fry until browned and softened.

MISCELLANEOUS

MAYONNAISE

Commercial mayonnaise is often filled with sugar! This recipe is delicious.

1 extra-large egg
  (organic, if possible)
3 tbsp white vinegar, OR (45 mL)
  lemon juice
1 tbsp water (15 mL)
3 tbsp SPLENDA® Granular (45 mL)
2 tsp prepared mustard (10 mL)
$^1/_2$ tsp dry mustard powder (2 mL)
$^1/_2$ tsp salt (2 mL)
$^1/_4$ tsp white pepper (1 mL)
$^1/_4$ tsp Thickening Agent, page 60 (1 mL)
1 cup light-tasting olive oil (250 mL)

> *Yield:* $1^1/_2$ cups (375 mL)
> 1 tbsp (15 mL) per serving
> 84.3 calories
> 0.3 g protein
> 9.3 g fat
> *0.4 g carbs*

In covered blender, blend egg, vinegar or lemon juice, water, SPLENDA®
Granular, mustard, dry mustard powder, salt and white pepper at low speed.
Uncover blender or through hole in lid, add Thickening Agent, page 60 and at
low speed in slow, steady stream, add olive oil, until mayonnaise is thoroughly
mixed and thickened.

Helpful Hints: Cider vinegar may be used instead of white vinegar, if desired.

85-90% Fat Fast: 1 tbsp (15 mL) per serving. (97.0% fat)

~~Low-Carb Dieting Tip~~
Plan, plan, plan your day and success will be yours.

MARMALADE

This marmalade is really excellent!

1 orange
1 lemon (or 2)
$^1/_4$ cup fresh lemon juice (50 mL)
19 oz crushed pineapple, (540 mL)
  in juice and undrained
$1^1/_2$ cups water (375 mL)
$^1/_2$ cup orange juice, (125 mL)
  from concentrate
$^1/_2$ tsp butter (2 mL)
$2^1/_2$ cups SPLENDA® Granular (625 mL)
1 package No Sugar Needed Fruit Pectin (49 g)
  (Bernardin)

Yield: $5^1/_2$ cups (1.375 L)
1 tsp (5 mL) per serving
3.5 calories
0.0 g protein
0.0 g fat
0.9 g carbs

Remove thin outer peel from orange with sharp paring knife. Discard as much white pith as possible. Chop peel finely. Chop orange finely. Remove thin outer peel from one lemon and extract fresh lemon juice (may need another lemon as well to make full amount of juice or just add a little water). Chop peel finely.

In large saucepan, place orange peel, lemon peel, lemon juice, crushed pineapple, water, orange juice and butter. Over high heat while stirring, bring to boil. Simmer 15 minutes over medium-low heat, stirring occasionally, until peel is soft. Add SPLENDA® Granular; stir well. Add pectin gradually; stir well.

Bring to full rolling boil. Boil 1 minute. Spoon marmalade into hot, sterilized jars and seal.

Helpful Hint: For longer storage, leave enough headspace in jar for expansion, and freeze, after jam has cooled.

~~*Low-Carb Dieting Tip*~~
An underactive thyroid is a common cause for slow weight loss.

CREAMY MUSTARD SAUCE

So easy to whip up. Great with baked ham.

$^3/_4$ cup sour cream (175 mL)
$^1/_4$ cup Mayonnaise, page 58 (50 mL)
$^1/_4$ cup prepared mustard (50 mL)

> **Yield:** $1^1/_4$ cups (300 mL)
> 1 tbsp (15 mL) per serving
> 32.3 calories
> 0.5 g protein
> 3.2 g fat
> ***0.5 g carbs***

In small bowl, combine sour cream, mayonnaise and mustard. Whisk until smooth. Refrigerate until serving time.

Helpful Hint: **85-90% Fat Fast:** 1 tbsp (15 mL) per serving. (87.6% fat)

THICKENING AGENT

This is useful to use instead of pure cornstarch or flour in thickening sauces.

$8^1/_2$ tsp xanthan gum (42 mL)
$4^1/_2$ tsp guar gum (22 mL)
$2^1/_4$ tsp corn starch (11 mL)

> **Yield:** $^1/_3$ cup (75 mL)
> 1 tsp (5 mL) per serving
> 1.5 calories
> 0.0 g protein
> 0.0 g fat
> ***0.4 g carbs***

In small plastic container with lid, combine xanthan gum, guar gum and cornstarch; seal. Store at room temperature.

Helpful Hints: Substitute Thickening Agent for cornstarch, using $^1/_4$ as much and substitute Thickening Agent for flour, using $^1/_8$ as much to achieve approximately the same results.

This Thickening Agent must be used in small quantities to avoid a "gummy" texture. For instance, do not use in quantities greater than $^1/_2$ tsp (2 mL) for thickening sauces for stir-fried vegetables. You may use only guar gum or only xanthan gum, if one or the other is not available.

CURRY POWDER

Making one's own curry powder is fun. My husband was so impressed.

$^1/_3$ cup ground turmeric (75 mL)
$^1/_3$ cup ground cumin (75 mL)
$^1/_3$ cup ground ginger (75 mL)
$^1/_4$ cup hot chili powder (50 mL)

> **Yield:** $1^1/_8$ cups (275 mL)
> 1 tsp (5 mL) per serving
> 7.2 calories
> 0.2 g protein
> 0.3 g fat
> **1.0 g carbs**

In medium bowl, combine turmeric, cumin, ginger and hot chili powder. Stir well. Store in closed container or sealed plastic bag at room temperature.

Variation: **Mild Curry Powder:** For milder curry powder, use 2 tbsp (25 mL) hot chili powder. (*1.0 g Carbs*)

BARBECUE SAUCE

Specifically created for Barbecue Chicken Pizza, page 38.

$^1/_2$ of $5^1/_2$ oz can tomato paste (78 mL)
3 tbsp white vinegar (45 mL)
2 tbsp SPLENDA® Granular (25 mL)
$^1/_2$ tsp onion salt (2 mL)
$^1/_2$ tsp Worcestershire sauce (2 mL)
$^1/_4$ tsp liquid smoke (1 mL)
$^1/_8$ tsp garlic powder (0.5 mL)
$^1/_8$ tsp black pepper (0.5 mL)

> **Yield:** $^1/_2$ cup (125 mL)
> 1 tbsp (15 mL) per serving
> 11.7 calories
> 0.4 g protein
> 0.1 g fat
> **2.3 g carbs**

In cereal bowl, combine tomato paste, vinegar, SPLENDA® Granular, onion salt, Worcestershire sauce, liquid smoke, garlic powder and black pepper. Mix well.

~~Low-Carb Dieting Tip~~
Too much carbohydrate leads to overeating.

MAYONNAISE SALAD DRESSING

A creamy dressing with that great mayonnaise taste!

$^1/_2$ cup plain yogurt (125 mL)
$^1/_3$ cup sour cream (75 mL)
$^1/_3$ cup mayonnaise, page 58 (75 mL)
2 tbsp white vinegar (25 mL)
1 tbsp SPLENDA® Granular (15 mL)
$^1/_2$ tsp dry mustard (2 mL)
$^1/_4$ tsp salt (1 mL)
$^1/_8$ tsp white pepper (0.5 mL)

> *Yield:* $1^1/_4$ cups (300 mL)
> 2 tbsp per serving (25 mL)
> 77.8 calories
> 0.9 g protein
> 7.8 g fat
> *1.1 g carbs*

In medium bowl, combine yogurt, sour cream, mayonnaise, page 58, vinegar, SPLENDA® Granular, dry mustard, salt and pepper. Stir well. Refrigerate in closed container.

Helpful Hint: **85-90% Fat Fast:** 1 serving. (89.6% fat)

HEALTHY BUTTER

This is a clever way to make butter healthier and higher in mononunsaturated fats. The taste is superb, plus it spreads easily straight from the refrigerator. My friend, Mary Converse, from Great Falls, Montana gave me this idea.

1 lb butter, softened (0.454 kg)
$1^1/_2$ cups olive oil (375 mL)

> *Yield:* 3 cups (750 mL)
> 1 tsp (5 mL) per serving
> 42.5 calories
> 0.0 g protein
> 4.8 g fat
> *0.0 g carbs*

In blender, process butter and olive oil until soft, creamy and smooth. Using spatula, scrape out into plastic bowl with lid and refrigerate until firm.

~~~Low-Carb Dieting Tip~~

Eat only when hungry.

BREADS, BAKE MIXES AND MUFFINS

SAVORY CHEESE BISCUITS

These are super! You will feel like you're cheating! Use it instead of English muffins, for instance, for an Eggs Benedict breakfast.

$1\frac{1}{2}$ cups Protein Bake Mix, (375 mL)
  page 68
1 tbsp soy flour (15 mL)
1 tbsp baking powder (15 mL)
$\frac{1}{2}$ tsp garlic powder (2 mL)
$\frac{1}{4}$ tsp basil (1 mL)
$\frac{1}{4}$ tsp dried parsley (1 mL)
$\frac{1}{4}$ tsp salt (1 mL)
$1\frac{1}{2}$ cups grated Cheddar cheese (375 mL)
3 eggs, fork beaten
$\frac{1}{2}$ cup whipping cream (125 mL)
2 tbsp olive oil (25 mL)

Yield: 12 Cheese Biscuits
1 Cheese Biscuit
175.6 calories
13.7 g protein
12.8 g fat
2.8 g carbs

In medium bowl, combine Protein Bake Mix, page 68, soy flour, baking powder, garlic powder, basil, dried parsley and salt. Stir in Cheddar cheese. In small bowl, combine eggs, whipping cream and olive oil. Stir into cheese mixture until moistened.

Drop batter by approximately 3 tablespoonful (45 mL) mounds onto greased cookie sheet, spaced about 2 inches (5 cm) apart to allow for spreading. Bake in 375°F (190°C) oven 15 minutes, or until golden brown. Serve warm with butter.

Variation: **Plain Cheese Biscuits:** Use 1 tbsp (15 mL) SPLENDA® Granular and $\frac{1}{2}$ tsp (2 mL) vanilla extract. Omit garlic powder, basil and dried parsley. These scone-like biscuits may be served with butter and sugarless jam. They make a great breakfast for a change of pace; high in protein and low in carbohydrates. Toast Savory Cheese Biscuit halves and put a fried egg on top – makes a good "toast" substitute. (*2.9 g Carbs*)

ZUCCHINI BRAN MINI MUFFINS

One of these for breakfast makes a nice change from eggs. Great fiber!

1 1/4 cups wheat bran (300 mL)
3/4 cup Protein Bake Mix, OR (175 mL)
   Whey Bake Mix, page 68
1/2 cup SPLENDA® Granular (125 mL)
1 tbsp baking powder (15 mL)
1 tsp cinnamon (5 mL)
1/8 tsp salt (0.5 mL)
1/2 cup grated zucchini (125 mL)
2 eggs, fork beaten
1/3 cup whipping cream (75 mL)
1/4 cup Healthy Butter, page 62, melted, OR (50 mL)
   use half butter and half olive oil
1 tsp vanilla extract (5 mL)

Yield: 12 mini muffins
1 mini muffin/PBM/WBM
120.6/111.1 calories
7.0/6.6 g protein
8.5/7.3 g fat
4.02/4.2 g carbs

In large bowl, combine wheat bran, Protein or Whey Bake Mix, page 68, SPLENDA® Granular, baking powder, cinnamon and salt. Stir in grated zucchini. In small bowl combine eggs, whipping cream, Healthy Butter, page 62 and vanilla extract. Add to wheat bran mixture, stirring just until moist. Add 1 tbsp (15 mL) water, if necessary. Overfill 12 greased mini muffin cups with batter and bake in 350°F (180°C) oven 15 minutes, or until slightly firm to the touch.

Variation: **Pumpkin Bran Mini Muffins:** Omit zucchini, Healthy Butter and cinnamon; add 1/3 cup (75 mL) mashed, cooked and slightly drained pumpkin and 1 tsp (5 mL) pumpkin pie spice. Add 1/4 cup (50 mL) chopped pecans. (***4.5 g Carbs***)

Helpful Hints: Refrigerate muffins for longer storage. Heat one in microwave oven 15 seconds, butter and enjoy! Freeze muffins, if desired, for no longer than 2 months. Microwave one frozen muffin 30 seconds, butter and enjoy! For half the fat, omit Healthy Butter altogether and use 2 to 3 tbsp (25 mL to 45 mL) water instead.

~~Low-Carb Dieting Tip~~
Adjust your caloric intake as you approach goal weight.

LEMON RICOTTA MUFFINS

These are like a scone or shortcake – absolutely yummy!

12 oz ricotta cheese (375 g)
$^1/_2$ cup butter, melted (125 mL)
2 eggs, fork beaten
1 tbsp fresh lemon juice (15 mL)
1 tsp finely chopped lemon rind (5 mL)
$^1/_4$ tsp lemon extract (1 mL)
1 cup Ultimate Bake Mix, (250 mL)
  page 67
$^1/_4$ cup SPLENDA® Granular (50 mL)
1 tbsp baking powder (15 mL)
$^1/_8$ tsp salt (0.5 mL)

> **Yield:** 12 muffins
> 1 muffin
> 150.3 calories
> 6.8 g protein
> 12.0 g fat
> **4.6 g carbs**

In medium bowl, combine ricotta cheese, butter, eggs, lemon juice, lemon rind and lemon extract. In small bowl, combine Ultimate Bake Mix, page 67, SPLENDA® Granular, baking powder and salt. Add to ricotta cheese mixture; mix. Fill 12 muffin cups about $^3/_4$ full. Bake in 400°F (200°C) oven 20 minutes. Serve with Crème Fraiche, page 70 and fresh, sliced strawberries, if desired.

CHEESE "BREAD" STICKS

Served warm, these are reminiscent of cheese bread sticks.

6 oz light cream cheese, (180 g)
  softened
2 extra-large eggs
6 oz grated Cheddar cheese (180 g)
3 oz Parmesan cheese (90 g)
6 tbsp whey protein powder, (90 mL)
  (natural)
$^1/_3$ cup soy, OR spelt flour (75 mL)
$^1/_4$ tsp paprika (1 mL)

> **Yield:** 40 Cheese Sticks
> 1 Stick - soy/spelt flour
> 46.6/47.5 calories
> 3.6/3.4 g protein
> 3.4/3.3 g fat
> **0.6/0.9 g carbs**

In food processor with sharp blade or blender, process cream cheese until smooth. Add eggs; process. Add Cheddar cheese, Parmesan cheese, whey protein powder, soy or spelt flour and paprika; process.

Turn out into 9 x 13-inch (23 x 33 cm) glass baking dish and press down evenly, using plastic wrap, to make things easier. Remove plastic wrap. Bake in 350°F (180°C) oven 15 to 20 minutes, or until turning golden brown at edges and when it is firm to the touch. From long side of dish, cut into 20, $^1/_2$ –inch (1.2 cm) sticks and cut down center of dish horizontally. Serve warm. Refrigerate leftovers and reheat Cheese "Bread" Sticks in microwave oven about 15 seconds.

WHOLEGRAIN BREAD

For crustier buns, toast lightly on both sides in nonstick pan.

1 cup water (250 mL)
3 tbsp olive oil (45 mL)
1 large egg
1 cup vital wheat gluten (250 mL)
$^2/_3$ cup whole wheat pastry flour, (150 mL)
  OR oat flour
$^1/_2$ cup wheat OR oat bran (125 mL)
$^1/_4$ cup whole wheat pastry four, (50 mL)
  OR flax seeds, ground, OR
  oat flour, OR soy flour
4 tsp bread machine yeast (20 mL)
1 tbsp SPLENDA® Granular (15 mL)
1 tbsp granulated sugar (15 mL)
1 tsp salt (5 mL)
1 tsp vanilla extract (5 mL)
1 tsp baking powder (5 mL)

Yield: 18 slices
Whole wheat/flax/oat flour
73.8/80.7/69.6 calories
6.7/6.9/6.5 g protein
2.8/3.6/2.8g fat
4.9/4.5/5.0 g carbs

In cereal bowl, heat water in microwave oven 1 minute. In bread pan, place water, olive oil, egg, vital wheat gluten, whole wheat pastry flour (or oat flour), wheat or oat bran, ground flax seeds (or whole wheat pastry flour, oat flour or soy flour), yeast, SPLENDA® Granular, sugar, salt, vanilla extract and baking powder. Program bread machine to Bread Rapid setting and color to medium. Remove 30 minutes before baking time is over or when brown in color.

Variations: **Loaf Pan Breads (Two):** Use 1 cup (250 mL) water, plus 3 tbsp (45 mL), 2 eggs, $1^1/_4$ cups (300 mL) 80% vital wheat gluten and 2 tsp (10 mL) baking powder. Follow recipe above with these changes. Program bread machine to pizza cycle. Divide dough in two equal portions. Place each portion in greased 9 x 5 x 3-inch (2 L) loaf pan and place pans on bottom shelf in preheated 225°F (107°C) oven which is off. Cover lightly with foil. Allow to rise 40 minutes. Remove foil; switch on oven to 350°F (180°C), leaving loaves inside. Bake 30 minutes. Place loaves on cake rack to cool. Place in paper bag and leave at room temperature for crusty loaves. Refrigerate for longer storage or freeze. *Yield:* 2 Loaves, 22 slices each, 1 slice per serving. (*2.0 g Carbs*)

Hamburger Buns, Hot Dog Buns or Dinner Rolls: Same recipe as for Loaf Pan Breads above. Shape dough into 12 hamburger or 9 hot dog buns or 24 dinner rolls. Place on greased pizza pan. Spray buns with nonstick cooking spray. Proceed as above and bake 20 minutes. *Yield:* 12 Hamburger buns. (*7.4 g Carbs*), 9 hot dog buns (*9.9 g Carbs*) or 24 Dinner Rolls. (*3.7 g Carbs*)

ULTIMATE BAKE MIX

This bake mix may be substituted cup-for-cup for all-purpose white wheat flour. It may be used to reduce carbohydrates in the recipes in my books, Splendid Desserts and More Splendid Desserts by 50 to 65%.

Soy Ultimate Bake Mix:
1 cup ground almonds, OR (250 mL)
  ground hazelnuts, pecans or walnuts
$^2/_3$ cup spelt, OR all-purpose, (150 mL)
  whole spelt or whole wheat flour
$^2/_3$ cup soy flour (150 mL)
$^1/_4$ cup vital wheat gluten (50 mL)

Yield: $2^3/_4$ cups (675 mL)
$^1/_4$ cup (50 mL) per serving
115.4 calories
7.7 g protein
6.1 g fat
8.0 g carbs

In medium bowl, combine ground almonds (hazelnuts, pecans or walnuts), spelt flour (all-purpose, whole spelt or whole wheat flour), soy flour and vital wheat gluten. Stir with wooden spoon to mix very well.

Variations: **Whey Ultimate Bake Mix (soy-free):** Combine 1 cup (250 mL) ground almonds or hazelnuts, etc., 1 cup (250 mL) spelt or all-purpose flour, etc., $^2/_3$ cup (150 mL) natural whey protein powder and 6 tbsp (90 mL) vital wheat gluten. *Yield:* 3 cups (750 mL), $^1/_4$ cup (50 mL) per serving. (***7.9 g Carbs***)

Oat Ultimate Bake Mix: Mix 1 cup (250 mL) ground hazelnuts, 1 cup (250 mL) oat flour, $^2/_3$ cup (150 mL) natural whey protein and 6 tbsp (90 mL) vital wheat gluten. *Yield:* 3 cups (750 mL), $^1/_4$ cup (50 mL) per serving. (***7.1 g Carbs***)

Self-Raising Soy Ultimate Bake Mix/Whey Ultimate Bake Mix: To convert Ultimate Bake Mix into a substitute for self-raising cake and pastry flour, substitute this recipe for equally good results: 1 cup (250 mL) Ultimate Bake Mix, $1^1/_2$ tsp (7 mL) baking powder and $^1/_3$ tsp (1.5 mL) salt. Therefore, for instance, when substituting Ultimate Bake Mix for $2^1/_2$ cups (625 mL) self-raising cake and pastry flour, use $2^1/_2$ cups (625 mL) Ultimate Bake Mix, $3^3/_4$ tsp (19 mL) baking powder and $^3/_4$ tsp (3 mL) salt to convert to self-raising.

Helpful Hints: Use this flavorful bake mix in your own favorite recipes! Typically, use $^1/_4$ cup (50 mL) or up to $^1/_2$ cup (125 mL) less liquid in recipes; add liquid cautiously! Using Soy Ultimate Bake Mix, replace some of butter in recipes with whipping cream – especially in cookie recipes to prevent a dry, powdery texture. With Whey Ultimate Bake Mix, replace half butter with olive oil in recipes, to keep baked goods moist. For some baking, replace natural whey protein with sucralose-sweetened vanilla or chocolate whey protein, if desired.

PROTEIN BAKE MIX

This is an easy good-tasting no-fuss bake mix. It makes moist baked goods. Many upscale health food stores will sell ground hazelnuts. The advantage, of course, is that this bake mix is particularly low in carbs.

1 cup low-fat soy flour (250 mL)
1 cup whey protein powder, (250 mL)
  (natural)
$^3/_4$ cup ground hazelnuts, OR (175 mL)
  ground almonds
$^1/_2$ cup soy protein isolate (125 mL)
2 tbsp SPLENDA® Granular (25 mL)
$^1/_4$ tsp salt (1 mL)

> **Yield:** $3^1/_2$ cups (875 mL)
> $^1/_4$ cup (50 mL) per serving
> 132.2 calories
> 18.6 g protein
> 5.8 g fat
> **3.5 g carbs**

In medium bowl, combine soy flour, whey protein powder, ground hazelnuts or almonds, soy protein isolate, SPLENDA® Granular and salt. Mix well. Use as directed in recipes.

WHEY BAKE MIX

This is a wonderful alternative for the above bake mix for folks who do not care for soy products in baking or who suffer from hypothyroidism.

$1^1/_4$ cups whey protein powder, (300 mL)
  (natural)
1 cup whole wheat pastry flour (250 mL)
$^3/_4$ cup ground hazelnuts, OR (175 mL)
  ground almonds
$^1/_4$ cup 80% vital wheat gluten (50 mL)
$^1/_4$ tsp salt (1 mL)

> **Yield:** $3^1/_2$ cups (875 mL)
> $^1/_4$ cup (50 mL) per serving
> 105.1 calories
> 9.7 g protein
> 5.0 g fat
> **5.5 g carbs**

In medium bowl, combine whey protein powder, whole wheat pastry flour, ground hazelnuts or almonds, vital wheat gluten and salt. Mix well.

Helpful Hints: Ground almonds may be used instead, however I just prefer the blander-tasting hazelnuts in these bake mixes. (Some health food stores, such as mine, provide ground hazelnuts for purchase. It's worth asking the store manager whether they can provide this service.) Many recipes can use either bake mix, however, sometimes I indicate in the Helpful Hints when one of these bake mixes is not suitable.

ICE CREAMS AND PUDDINGS

COCONUT CHOCOLATE MOUSSE

This dessert forms a soft set, more like a regular chocolate pudding, but with a richer, more velvety texture.

8 oz light cream cheese, softened (250 g)
2 cups fresh coconut milk, (500 mL)
  page 41, OR canned coconut milk
$^3/_4$ cup SPLENDA® Granular (175 mL)
$^1/_3$ cup cocoa (75 mL)
1 tsp vanilla extract (5 mL)
1 envelope unflavored gelatin (15 mL)
$^1/_4$ cup cold water (50 mL)
$^3/_4$ cup boiling water (175 mL)

Yield: 10 servings
1 serving
161.1 calories
3.9 g protein
15.0 g fat (78.2%)
4.2 g carbs

In food processor with sharp blade, blender or in bowl with electric mixer, process cream cheese. Add coconut milk, SPLENDA® Granular, cocoa and vanilla extract. Process, scraping sides occasionally. In medium bowl, soften gelatin in cold water. Stir in boiling water, until gelatin dissolves. Add to cream cheese mixture; process. Pour into 9-inch (23 cm) glass pie dish and chill until the mousse forms a soft set.

Variation: **Coconut Mousse:** Omit cocoa. Use $1^1/_2$ envelopes unflavored gelatin. (***3.9 g Carbs***)

Helpful Hints: **75-80% Fat Fast: Coconut Chocolate Mousse:** 1 serving. (Use the above recipe or use $^1/_4$ cup (50 mL) SPLENDA® Granular and $^1/_2$ cup (125 mL) Da Vinci® Sugar Free Coconut syrup to replace an equivalent amount of water.) (156.3 calories, 3.9 g protein, 15.0 g fat (80.4%), 3.0 g carbs)

Coconut Mousse: 1 serving.
(156.9 calories, 3.6 g protein, 14.8 g fat (81.6%), 3.9 g carbs)

~~Low-Carb Dieting Tip~~
Water retention masks fat loss.

CRÈME FRAICHE

Lovely sweetened whipped topping for serving with desserts or fruit or for garnishing desserts. It holds up better than plain whipped cream. Double Thickening agent, page 60, for Crème Fraiche with even greater hold.

1 cup whipping cream (250 mL)
$\frac{1}{2}$ cup SPLENDA® Granular (125 mL)
$\frac{1}{4}$ tsp Thickening Agent, page 60 (1 mL)
  (optional)
$\frac{2}{3}$ cup regular sour cream, OR (150 mL)
  nonfat sour cream
$\frac{1}{2}$ tsp vanilla extract (2 mL)

> *Yield:* 2$\frac{1}{8}$ cups (525 mL)
> 2 tbsp (25 mL) per serving
> 56.2 calories
> 0.5 g protein
> 5.4 g fat
> *1.5 g carbs*

In food processor, on low speed, process whipping cream with SPLENDA® Granular. While processing, sprinkle in Thickening Agent, page 60, if using, through feed tube. Process until stiff. Add sour cream and vanilla extract; process on medium high speed just until combined. It will keep at least one week or longer in refrigerator.

Variation: **Chocolate Pudding:** Add $\frac{1}{2}$ cup (125 mL) Chocolate Whey Protein Powder and $\frac{1}{4}$ cup (50 mL) SPLENDA® Granular.
Yield: 2 $\frac{1}{4}$ cups (550 mL), 9 tbsp (135 mL) per serving. (*4.9 g Carbs*)

75-80% Fat Fast: Chocolate Pudding: 9 tbsp (135 mL) per serving. ($\frac{1}{2}$ cup (125 mL) = 8 tbsp) (225.5 calories, 7.1 g protein, 20.0 g fat (83.2%), 4.9 g carbs)

85-90% Fat Fast: Any Flavor Pudding: Use $\frac{1}{4}$ cup (50 mL) Da Vinci® Sugar Free Flavored syrup such as caramel, toasted marshmallow, cherry, vanilla, etc. instead of SPLENDA® Granular. Increase Thickening Agent to $\frac{3}{4}$ tsp (3 mL). Omit vanilla extract. Add syrup along with sour cream; process.
Yield: 2$\frac{1}{4}$ cups (550 mL), 9 tbsp (135 mL) per serving.
(239.4 calories, 2.4 g protein, 24.5 g fat (90.3%), 3.5 g carbs)

Helpful Hints: Thickening Agent, page 60 makes Crème Fraiche firmer and easier to garnish desserts using a pastry bag. Double Thickening Agent in this recipe for garnishing desserts. Recipe may easily be doubled or halved. Half this recipe will suffice as a topping for a cheesecake.
Yield: 12 servings. (*1.1 g Carbs*)

~~Low-Carb Dieting Tip~~

The scale does not tell the whole story. Take your measurements periodically. Work out your body fat percentage.

LINDA'S ICE CREAM CUSTARD

I credit my American friend, Linda Parsons, with the idea for this recipe.

2 extra-large eggs
$^3/_4$ cup SPLENDA® Granular (175 mL)
$^1/_2$ cup ice cold water (125 mL)
2 tbsp vanilla extract (25 mL)
2 cups whipping cream, (500 mL)
$^1/_8$ tsp salt (0.5 mL)
$^1/_8$ tsp guar gum, (0.5 mL)
  (optional)

Yield: $4^1/_2$ cups (1.125L)
$^1/_2$ cup (125 mL) per serving
193.3 calories
2.5 g protein
18.1 g fat (86.0%)
4.1 g carbs

Coddle eggs: Place eggs in boiling water one minute and remove.

In large bowl, whisk eggs with wire whisk a couple of minutes, until light and frothy. In small bowl, combine SPLENDA® Granular, cold water and vanilla; whisk in with eggs. In food processor, whip cream with salt and guar gum until stiff. Fold in whipped cream. Freeze in ice cream maker as manufacturer directs. Freeze leftovers.

Variations: **Strawberry:** Use 1 cup (250 mL) frozen unsweetened strawberries, slightly thawed. Blend in blender with cold water mixture; stir into whisked eggs. Add red food coloring, if desired.
Yield: $5^1/_2$ cups (1.4 L), $^1/_2$ cup (125 mL) per serving. (***4.3 g Carbs***)

Any Flavor (using Da Vinci® Sugar Free Flavors): Use $^2/_3$ cup (150 mL) any flavor Da Vinci® Sugar Free Syrup. Omit ice cold water and vanilla extract.
Yield: $4^1/_2$ cups (1 .125L), $^1/_2$ cup (125 mL) per serving. (***1.8 g Carbs***)

French Vanilla: Add three extra egg yolks (from coddled eggs).
Yield: 5 cups (1.25 L), $^1/_2$ cup (125 mL) per serving. (***3.8 g Carbs***)

Chocolate: In blender, combine 1 cup (250 mL) SPLENDA® Granular, $^1/_4$ cup (50 mL) cocoa, cold water, eggs and 1 tsp (5 mL) vanilla extract; blend. Fold in whipped cream.
Yield: 5 cups (1.25 L), $^1/_2$ cup (125 mL) per serving. (***4.3 g Carbs***)
With $^1/_2$ cup (125 mL) SPLENDA® Granular and $^2/_3$ cup (150 mL) Da Vinci® Sugar Free Flavored syrup (omit water).
Yield: 5 cups (1.25 L), $^1/_2$ cup (125 mL) per serving. (***3.1 g Carbs***)

Helpful Hints: **85-90% Fat Fast:** $^1/_2$ cup (125 mL) per serving. (Obviously, the best choice is Any Flavor Ice Cream sweetened with Da Vinci® Sugar Free Flavors, however, any of these ice creams are fine.)
(177.0 calories, 2.5 g protein, 18.1 g fat (90.5 %), 1.8 g carbs)

CRÈME CARAMEL CUSTARD

A fabulous recipe for induction or 80-90% Fat Fast.

4 eggs
$2^1/_2$ cups whipping cream (625 mL)
$^1/_2$ cup Da Vinci® Sugar Free (125 mL)
  Caramel syrup
1 tsp vanilla extract (5 mL)

Yield: 10 servings.
1 serving
211.6 calories
3.7 g protein
21.1 g fat
2.2 g carbs

In medium bowl, whisk eggs until frothy. Stir in cream, Da Vinci® Sugar Free Caramel syrup and vanilla extract. Pour into glass pie dish or casserole dish. Bake in 350°F (180°C) oven 40 to 50 minutes, until set.

Variations: **Any Flavor Panna Cotta:** Omit eggs and vanilla extract. Use any flavor Da Vinci® Sugar Free syrup and 3 tsp (15 mL) unflavored gelatin. In cereal bowl, sprinkle gelatin over 3 tbsp (45 mL) cream to soften. Place remaining cream and Da Vinci® Sugar Free Flavored syrup in non-stick saucepan or in double boiler. Heat gently, stirring until scalding. Remove from heat and whisk in gelatin until dissolved. Pour into 6 individual molds or ramekins or into a 9-inch (23 cm) pie dish and chill 2 hours, or until set. Unmold by wiping a clean cloth dipped in hot water over the mold, and invert.
Yield: 6 servings. (***3.1 g Carbs***)

Blender Coconut Custard Pie: Add 1 cup (250 mL) unsweetened coconut , $^1/_4$ cup (50 mL) butter (melted), $^1/_2$ tsp (2 mL) baking powder and $^1/_4$ tsp (1 mL) salt. Use coconut-flavored syrup and use only $1^3/_4$ cups (425 mL) whipping cream. Omit vanilla extract. Place all ingredients in blender. Blend. Pour into 9-inch (23 cm) glass baking dish. Bake in 350°F (180°C) oven 45 minutes, or until golden brown on top. This custard forms its own crust. Great fiber!
Yield: 10 servings. (***2.1 g Carbs***)

Helpful Hints: **85-90% Fat Fast (Crème Caramel Custard):** 1 serving. (89.0% fat)

85-90% Fat Fast (Any Flavor Panna Cotta): 1 serving. (304.8 calories, 3.1 g protein, 31.9 g fat (92.1%), 3.1 g carbs)

85-90% Fat Fast (Blender Coconut Custard Pie): 1 serving. (264.2 calories, 4.1 g protein, 26.2 g fat (88.1 %), 2.1 g carbs)

VANILLA CREAM JELLY

A simple, scrumptious jelly.

1 cup water (250 mL)
1 tbsp unflavored gelatin (15 mL)
3 tbsp water (45 mL)
1 cup whipping cream (250 mL)
$^1/_3$ cup SPLENDA® Granular (75 mL)
1 tsp vanilla extract, OR (5 mL)
  maple extract

Yield: 4 servings
1 serving
211.8 calories
2.7 g protein
20.8 g fat (87.7%)
3.8 g carbs

In small saucepan, pour 1 cup (250 mL) water. Heat to scalding. In small bowl, soften gelatin in 3 tbsp (45 mL) water. Add to scalding water, stirring until dissolved. In medium bowl, combine cream, water with dissolved gelatin, SPLENDA® Granular and vanilla extract. Pour into mold and refrigerate until set.

Helpful Hint: **85-90% Fat Fast:** 1 serving. (Substitute $^1/_3$ cup (75 mL) water with $^1/_3$ cup (75 mL) Da Vinci® Sugar Free French Vanilla or Vanilla syrup and omit SPLENDA® Granular.)
(200.8 calories, 2.7 g protein, 20.8 g fat (91.4%), 1.7 g carbs)

ANY FLAVOR YOGURT JELLY

Pudding-like jelly pleases kids and adults alike.

$^1/_2$ cup SPLENDA® Granular (125 mL)
$1^1/_2$ envelopes unflavored gelatin
1 cup boiling water (250 mL)
2 cups plain yogurt (500 mL)
1 envelope any flavor Kool-Aid®,
  (sugar-free or add sugar variety)

Yield: 6 servings
1 serving
72.6 calories
5.0 g protein
2.7 g fat
3.5 g carbs

In medium bowl, combine SPLENDA® Granular, gelatin and boiling water. Combine yogurt and Kool-Aid®. Stir in. Pour into 4-cup (1 L) mold. Refrigerate until set.

CAKES, PIES AND CHEESECAKES

POUND CAKE

Moist, dense, delicious tender crumb cake

$^1/_2$ cup butter, softened (125 mL)
4 oz light cream cheese, softened (125 g)
4 extra-large eggs
1 tsp vanilla extract (5 mL)
1 tsp lemon extract (5 mL)
$1^3/_4$ cups ground almonds (425 mL)
$^1/_2$ cup Ultimate Bake Mix, (125 mL)
  page 67
1 cup SPLENDA® Granular (250 mL)
1 tbsp baking powder (15 mL)
3 tbsp water (45 mL)
2 tbsp whipping cream (25 mL)

Yield: 16 servings
1 serving
144.4 calories
5.9 g protein
11.2 g fat
5.5 g carbs

In food processor or using electric mixer, process butter and cream cheese until combined. Add eggs one at a time while processing. Add vanilla and lemon extracts; process. In medium bowl, combine ground almonds, Ultimate Bake Mix, page 67, SPLENDA® Granular and baking powder. Add half dry mixture to food processor or electric mixer along with water. Process until smooth. Add whipping cream and remaining dry mixture; process.

Line 10-inch (4 L) nonstick tube pan with parchment or wax paper (leaving edges high). Spray with nonstick cooking spray. Pour batter in carefully and smooth surface with back of spoon. Bake in 350°F (180°C) oven 30 to 35 minutes, or until cake tester inserted comes out clean. Turn out on cake rack to cool. Carefully remove paper.

Serving suggestion: Serve each piece of cake with sliced strawberries and Crème Fraiche, page 60, if desired.

Helpful Hint: The parchment or wax paper is to prevent this cake from sticking in the Bundt pan.

BLACK FOREST CAKE
Delicious, special occasion cake.

5 tbsp butter, softened (75 mL)
4 egg yolks
1 $^{1}/_{4}$ cups Ultimate Bake Mix, (300 mL)
  page 67 (with whey and hazelnuts)
$^{1}/_{3}$ cup cocoa (75 mL)
$^{3}/_{4}$ cup SPLENDA® Granular (175 mL)
2 $^{1}/_{2}$ tsp baking powder (12 mL)
6 egg whites
$^{1}/_{2}$ tsp cream of tartar (2 mL)
$^{1}/_{4}$ cup whipping cream (50 mL)
$^{1}/_{4}$ cup water (50 mL)

Yield: 12 servings
1 serving
226.5 calories
6.9 g protein
18.7 g fat
8.2 g carbs

Filling and Topping:
2 tbsp unsweetened pineapple juice (25 mL)
1 tbsp SPLENDA® Granular (15 mL)
$^{1}/_{2}$ tsp brandy extract (2 mL)
Crème Fraiche, page 70
20 fresh cherries

In food processor or electric mixer, cream butter and egg yolks. In medium bowl, combine Ultimate Bake Mix, page 67, cocoa, SPLENDA® Granular and baking powder.

Beat egg whites with cream of tartar until stiff. To egg yolk mixture, add dry ingredients and whipping cream and water in 2 additions, beating 1 minute after each addition, until smooth. Fold egg whites into cake batter and spoon equal amounts into 3 greased 8-inch (20 cm) round cake pans. Bake in 350°F (180°C) oven 15 to 20 minutes. Allow to cool in pans on cake racks. Carefully remove.

Filling and Topping: In small bowl, combine pineapple juice, SPLENDA® Granular and brandy extract. Sprinkle some over each cake layer. Spread bottom cake layer with Crème Fraiche, page 70 and place 10 cherries (pitted and cut in half) down. Repeat with next cake layer, ending with final layer and 10 whole cherries for garnish.

Helpful Hint: For a lower carb cake, use $^{1}/_{3}$ cup (75 mL) SPLENDA® Granular and $^{1}/_{3}$ cup (75 mL) Da Vinci® Sugar Free Chocolate syrup. Reduce cream to 3 tbsp (45 mL) and omit water. (***7.2 g Carbs***)

CINNAMON KUCHEN WITH BUTTER SAUCE

The secret to this recipe lies in the decadent sauce!

2 eggs, separated
$^1/_2$ cup SPLENDA® Granular (125 mL)
$^1/_4$ cup whipping cream (50 mL)
2 tbsp butter, melted (25 mL)
$^1/_2$ tsp vanilla extract (2 mL)
1 cup Ultimate Bake Mix, p. 67 (250 mL)
$1^1/_2$ tsp baking powder (7 mL)
1 tsp cinnamon (5 mL)
$^1/_8$ tsp salt (0.5 mL)

Walnut Topping:
2 tbsp walnut crumbs (25 mL)
1 tbsp SPLENDA® Granular (15 mL)
$^1/_8$ tsp cinnamon (0.5 mL)
1 tbsp butter, melted (15 mL)

Butter Sauce:
$^1/_3$ cup butter (75 mL)
$^1/_3$ cup whipping cream (75 mL)
$^1/_2$ cup SPLENDA® Granular (125 mL)
$^1/_8$ tsp vanilla extract (0.5 mL)

Yield: 12 servings
1 serving
177.0 calories
5.1 g protein
15.1 g fat
5.6 g carbs

Beat egg whites until stiff. Add egg yolks and SPLENDA® Granular gradually, beating until well combined. In small bowl, combine cream, butter and vanilla extract. In medium bowl, combine Ultimate Bake Mix, page 67, baking powder, cinnamon and salt. Stir cream mixture in and fold in egg mixture. Pour into well-greased 8-inch (20 cm) round cake pan. Sprinkle with Walnut Topping. Bake in 375°F (190°C) oven 15 minutes or until cake tester inserted in center comes out clean. Serve each slice with warm Butter Sauce.

Walnut Topping: In small bowl, combine walnut crumbs, SPLENDA® Granular, cinnamon and melted butter.

Butter Sauce: In small saucepan, melt butter. Stir in whipping cream and SPLENDA® Granular. Bring to boil. Remove from heat and add vanilla extract.

~~Low-Carb Dieting Tip~~
Have you taken your nutritional supplements today?

RHUBARB CHIFFON PIE

Excellent, pretty in pink, and slightly tart! My son, Jonathan, loved this pie.

Cookie Crust:
$^3/_4$ cup Whey Ultimate Bake (175 mL)
  Mix, page 67
1 tbsp SPLENDA® Granular (15 mL)
$^1/_4$ tsp baking soda (1 mL)
$2^1/_2$ tbsp butter, softened (32 mL)
1 oz regular cream cheese, softened (30 g)

Filling:
$2^1/_2$ cups chopped rhubarb (625 mL)
$^1/_2$ cup water (125 mL)
$^1/_4$ cup DaVinci® Sugar Free Syrup, (50 mL)
  Strawberry, OR Raspberry flavor
1 envelope PLUS $1^1/_2$ tsp unflavored gelatin (22 mL)
2 tbsp water (25 mL)
1 cup SPLENDA® Granular (250 mL)
1 cup whipping cream (250 mL)

Yield: 10 servings
1 serving
164.4 calories
4.9 g protein
13.3 g fat
7.0 g carbs

Cookie Crust: In small bowl, using electric mixer, beat Whey Ultimate Bake Mix, page 67, SPLENDA® Granular, baking soda, butter and cream cheese, until coarse crumbs form. Turn out on "floured" surface (use either whey protein powder or soy protein isolate). Roll and/or pat into 8-inch (20 cm) circle. Using lifter, lift carefully into shallow 9-inch (23 cm) glass pie dish. Using small rolling pin, roll and pat dough in evenly and up sides. "Flour" rolling pin as necessary. Set aside. With fork, prick crust all over. Bake in 350°F (180°C) oven 10 to 15 minutes or until browned slightly.

Filling: In medium saucepan, combine rhubarb, $^1/_2$ cup (125 mL) water and DaVinci® Syrup. Bring to boil, reduce heat slightly and cook until rhubarb is soft. In small bowl, soften gelatin in 2 tbsp (25 mL) water. Stir into hot rhubarb sauce until dissolved. Remove from heat; stir in SPLENDA® Granular. Pour into medium bowl and chill until syrupy. Whip cream until stiff. Fold into cooled rhubarb. Pour over crust; chill. Serve with Crème Fraiche, page 70.

Helpful Hints: Instead of DaVinci® Sugar Free Syrup, you could add water, Kool-Aid® flavoring and extra sweetener to taste.

75-80% Fat Fast: 2 servings.
(Omit crust. In filling omit water and SPLENDA® Granular. To sweeten, use $^3/_4$ cup (175 mL) Da Vinci® Sugar Free syrup in either strawberry, raspberry or cherry flavor.) (164.2 calories, 3.4 g protein, 15.4 g fat (82.1%), 4.2 g carbs)

FROZEN GRASSHOPPER PIE

Jonathan and Ian fought a friendly battle over the last piece!

Chocolate Crust:
1¹/₂ oz light cream cheese, (45 g)
  softened
2 tbsp unsalted butter, (25 mL)
  softened
¹/₄ cup cocoa (50 mL)
¹/₄ cup SPLENDA® Granular (50 mL)
3 tbsp vital wheat gluten (45 mL)
2 tbsp whipping cream (25 mL)

Yield: 10 servings
1 serving
280.7 calories
7.7 g protein
24.6 g fat
7.8 g carbs

Filling:
Condensed Milk, page 88
1 tsp peppermint extract (5 mL)
8 drops green food coloring
2¹/₂ cups Crème Fraiche, page 70 (625 mL)
  (omit Thickening Agent)
Chocolate Curls, (optional)
1 oz unsweetened or bittersweet baking chocolate (30 g)

Crust: In food processor, process cream cheese and butter until smooth. Add cocoa, SPLENDA® Granular, vital wheat gluten and whipping cream; process. Sprinkle in 9-inch (23 cm) springform pan or glass pie dish. Cover with plastic wrap and press crust out evenly. Press into bottom of 9-inch (23 cm) glass baking dish.

Filling: In large bowl, combine Condensed Milk, page 88, peppermint extract and green food coloring. Fold in Crème Fraiche, page 70 until evenly colored. Pour into prepared crust. Garnish with chocolate curls, if desired. Freeze 6 hours, or until firm. Allow to thaw a few minutes before cutting and serving.

Chocolate Curls (optional): Microwave 1 oz (30 g) unsweetened or bittersweet baking chocolate (or use sugar free chocolate bar) until melted (usually about 2 minutes). Spread chocolate thinly with knife over small, flat baking sheet or dinner plate. Freeze until firm enough to form curls when knife is dragged firmly across surface. If chocolate freezes too hard, curls will not form. Leave at room temperature for a few minutes and try again.

Helpful Hint: 75-80% Fat Fast: 1 serving. (Use Fat Fast Condensed Milk, page 88 and Fat Fast Crème Fraiche, page 70. Omit crust.)
(192.9 calories, 4.5 g protein, 18.1 g fat (83.9%), 3.3 g carbs)

FRENCH COCONUT PIE

If you like coconut, this pie will delight you with its wonderful texture and taste.

Cookie Crust:

$^3/_4$ cup Whey Ultimate Bake (175 mL)
   Mix, page 67
1 tbsp SPLENDA® Granular (15 mL)
$^1/_4$ tsp baking soda (1 mL)
$2^1/_2$ tbsp butter, softened (32 mL)
1 oz regular cream cheese, softened (30 g)

Filling:

3 extra-large eggs
$1^1/_4$ cups SPLENDA® Granular (300 mL)
$^1/_2$ cup butter, melted (125 mL)
1 tbsp lemon juice (15 mL)
1 tbsp French Vanilla DaVinci® Sugar (15 mL)
   Free Syrup (optional)
1 tsp vanilla extract (5 mL)
1 cup fine coconut, PLUS 2 tbsp (275 mL)
nutmeg sprinkle

Yield: 10 servings	
1 serving	
265.8 calories	
6.0 g protein	
23.1 g fat	
6.5 g carbs	

Cookie Crust: In small bowl, using electric mixer, beat Whey Ultimate Bake Mix, page 67, SPLENDA® Granular, baking soda, butter and cream cheese, until coarse crumbs form. Turn out on "floured" surface (use either whey protein powder or soy protein isolate). Roll and/or pat into 8-inch (20 cm) circle. Lift carefully into shallow 9-inch (23 cm) glass pie dish. Using small rolling pin, roll and pat dough in evenly and up sides. "Flour" rolling pin as necessary. Set aside.

Filling: In medium bowl, beat eggs with fork until frothy. Whisk in SPLENDA® Granular, butter, lemon juice, DaVinci® Sugar Free Syrup (if using) and vanilla extract. Stir in coconut. Pour into unbaked pie shell. Bake in 350°F (180°C) oven 20 to 30 minutes, or until crust is browned and filling is set. Sprinkle lightly with nutmeg. Serve either warm or chilled.

Helpful Hint: 75-80% Fat Fast: 1 serving.   (Omit Cookie Crust.)
(193.0 calories, 2.7 g protein, 17.6 g fat (82.1%), 3.9 g carbs)

~~Low-Carb Dieting Tip~~
Seasoned low-carbers have fine-tuned the diet to work better for them.

CHOCOLATE FUDGE CHEESECAKE
Not baked and no gelatin used – delicious milk chocolate flavor!

Chocolate Crust:
1 ¹/₂ oz light cream cheese, softened (45 g)
2 tbsp unsalted butter, softened (25 mL)
¹/₄ cup cocoa (50 mL)
¹/₄ cup SPLENDA® Granular (50 mL)
3 tbsp vital wheat gluten (45 mL)
2 tbsp whipping cream (25 mL)

Filling:
16 oz regular cream cheese, (500 g)
  softened
1 ³/₄ cups SPLENDA® Granular (425 mL)
1 cup whipping cream (250 mL)
¹/₄ cup whey protein powder (50 mL)
  (natural)
1 tsp Thickening Agent, page 60 (5 mL)
2 oz unsweetened baking chocolate, (30 g)
  melted
2 tsp vanilla extract (10 mL)

Yield: 12 servings
1 serving
279.9 calories
8.3 g protein
24.6 g fat
7.4 g carbs

Crust: In food processor, process cream cheese and butter until smooth. Add cocoa, SPLENDA® Granular, vital wheat gluten and whipping cream; process.

Sprinkle in 9-inch (23 cm) springform pan or glass pie dish. Cover with plastic wrap and press crust out evenly. Bake in 350°F (180°C) oven 5 minutes.

Filling: In food processor, process cream cheese until smooth. Add SPLENDA® Granular, whipping cream, whey protein powder and Thickening Agent, page 60. Process until thickened. Add chocolate and vanilla extract. Process until very smooth. Pour over crust. Form pattern on surface of cheesecake with tines of dinner fork. Sprinkle sparsely with grated unsweetened chocolate, if desired. Refrigerate preferably 2 days before serving.

Helpful Hints: 75-80% Fat Fast: 1 serving. (Omit crust. Use 1 ¹/₄ cups (300 mL) SPLENDA® Granular, ¹/₂ cup (125 mL) Da Vinci® Sugar Free Chocolate syrup and omit cream.) (169.6 calories, 5.7 g protein, 14.5 g fat (74.8%), 4.6 g carbs) With ¹/₂ cup (125 mL) cream, this is a **Chocolate Mousse** (Try it as a frozen dessert; allow to thaw a few minutes before serving.). (199.7 cal., 77.6% fat)

~~Low-Carb Dieting Tip~~
Our goal weight and our "natural" weight can differ by quite a few pounds.

DELUXE BAKED CHEESECAKE

This cheesecake is extremely rich, but unbelievably good! Cut smaller servings.

Crust:
$^1/_2$ cup ground almonds (125 mL)
2 tbsp SPLENDA® Granular (25 mL)
1 tbsp soy, OR spelt flour (15 mL)
2 tbsp butter, melted (25 mL)
1 egg yolk

Filling:
5, 8-oz packages cream cheese, (1.25 kg)
  (regular), softened
$1^3/_4$ cups SPLENDA® Granular (425 mL)
$^1/_4$ cup whipping cream (50 mL)
3 egg yolks
1 tbsp vanilla extract (15 mL)

Chocolate Glaze:
1.1 oz maltitol chocolate (34 g)
  (sugar free chocolate)
$^1/_2$ oz unsweetened chocolate (15 g)
2 tbsp unsalted butter (25 mL)
3 tbsp whipping cream (45 mL)
2 tbsp SPLENDA® Granular, (optional) (25 mL)
$^1/_2$ tsp vanilla extract (2 mL)

Yield: 16 servings
1 serving
345.5 calories
9.1 g protein
31.7 g fat
6.4 g carbs

Crust: In medium bowl, combine ground almonds, SPLENDA® Granular and soy or spelt flour. Stir in butter and egg yolk. In 9-inch (23 cm) springform pan, cover with plastic wrap; press crust out. Bake in 350°F (180°C) oven 5 minutes.

Filling: In food processor with sharp blade or electric mixer, process cream cheese until smooth. Add SPLENDA® Granular, whipping cream, egg yolks, and vanilla extract; process. Pour over crust. Bake in 350°F (180°C) oven on middle shelf 40 minutes. Turn oven down to 300°F (150°C) and bake another 10 minutes on bottom shelf. Run sharp knife around edges.

Chocolate Glaze: In double boiler, melt maltitol chocolate, unsweetened chocolate and butter. Stir in whipping cream, SPLENDA® Granular (if using) and vanilla extract until smooth and thick. Pour over cooled cheesecake and spread evenly. Leave edges bare for garnishing with Crème Fraiche, page 70.

Helpful Hint: 75-80% Fat Fast: 1 serving. (Omit crust, cream, vanilla extract and chocolate glaze. Use $1^1/_4$ cups (300 mL) SPLENDA® Granular and $^1/_4$ cup (50 mL) Da Vinci® Sugar Free Flavored syrup.)
(254.9 calories, 7.6 g protein, 23.2 g fat (81.4%), 4.3 g carbs)

STRAWBERRY CHOCOLATE SWIRL CHEESECAKE

Each bite is like enjoying a delectable strawberry chocolate truffle.

Crust:
$^1/_2$ cup ground almonds, (125 mL)
2 tbsp SPLENDA® Granular (25 mL)
1 tbsp soy, OR spelt flour (15 mL)
2 tbsp butter, melted (25 mL)
1 egg yolk

Filling:
16 oz reg. cream cheese, softened (500 g)
8 oz light cream cheese, softened (250 g)
1 cup sour cream (250 mL)
1 cup SPLENDA® Granular (250 mL)
2 eggs
2 tsp vanilla extract (10 mL)
$^1/_4$ cup cocoa (50 mL)
$^1/_4$ cup SPLENDA® Granular (50 mL)
1 tbsp vegetable oil (15 mL)
$^2/_3$ cup frozen unsweetened strawberries, thawed (150 mL)
$^1/_2$ cup SPLENDA® Granular (125 mL)
$^1/_8$ tsp Thickening Agent, page 60 (0.5 mL)
2 tbsp vital wheat gluten (25 mL)

Yield: 12/16 servings
1 serving
297.6/223.5 calories
10.4 g/7.8 g protein
24.6 g/18.5 g fat
8.8 g/6.5 g carbs

Crust: In medium bowl, combine ground almonds, SPLENDA® Granular and soy or spelt flour. Stir in butter and egg yolk. In 9-inch (23 cm) springform pan, cover with plastic wrap; press crust out. Bake in 350°F (180°C) oven 5 minutes.

Filling: In food processor with sharp blade, blender or in bowl with electric mixer, process cream cheeses until smooth. Add sour cream, 1 cup (250 mL) SPLENDA® Granular, eggs and vanilla extract; process. In small bowl, stir $1^1/_2$ cups (375 mL) batter, cocoa, $^1/_4$ cup (50 mL) SPLENDA® Granular and oil together. In blender, blend strawberries, $^1/_2$ cup (125 mL) SPLENDA® Granular, and Thickening Agent, page 60 until smooth. Add to remaining batter, along with vital wheat gluten; process. Seal springform pan with foil all around. Pour half strawberry mixture over crust, dollop with half chocolate mixture over top; repeat. Swirl through layers. Bake in water bath (place in larger pan with boiling water coming about 1-inch (2.5 cm) up sides of springform pan) 10 minutes in 400°F (200°C) oven. Reduce heat to 250°F (120°C); bake 55 minutes. Garnish with chocolate curls, page 78, and glazed strawberries.

Helpful Hint: 75-80% Fat Fast: Yield: 12 servings. (Omit crust, omit strawberries. Use $^1/_4$ cup (50 mL) Da Vinci® Sugar Free Strawberry syrup instead.) (186.5 calories, 6.2 g protein, 15.7 g fat (74.7%), 5.2 g carbs)

BLACK FOREST CHEESECAKE

Many people prefer a cheesecake containing ricotta cheese. This one has a marbled effect. This cheesecake gets better as it ages!

Almond Crust:
$^1/_2$ cup ground almonds (125 mL)
2 tbsp SPLENDA® Granular (25 mL)
1 tbsp soy, OR spelt flour (15 mL)
2 tbsp butter, melted (25 mL)
1 egg yolk

Filling:
2 cups ricotta cheese (500 mL)
12 oz regular cream cheese, softened (375 g)
$^1/_2$ cup sour cream (125 mL)
$1^1/_4$ cups SPLENDA® Granular (300 mL)
3 eggs
10 cherries, pitted and cut in half
$^1/_4$ cup cocoa (50 mL)
$^1/_4$ cup chocolate whey protein powder (50 mL)
2 tbsp Da Vinci® Sugar Free Chocolate syrup (25 mL)
1 tbsp whipping cream (15 mL)
1 tsp Thickening Agent, page 60 (5 mL)

Garnish:
whipped cream and additional
  cherries, if desired

Yield: 12 servings
1 serving
227.6 calories
12.2 g protein
16.6 g fat
8.2 g carbs

Almond Crust: In medium bowl, combine ground almonds, SPLENDA® Granular and soy or spelt flour. Stir in butter and egg yolk. Sprinkle in 9-inch (23 cm) glass pie dish or springform pan. Cover with plastic wrap and press crust out evenly; remove plastic wrap. Bake in 350°F (180°C) oven 10 minutes or until turning brown at edges.

Filling: In food processor with sharp blade, blender or in bowl with electric mixer, process ricotta cheese until smooth. Add cream cheese, sour cream, SPLENDA® Granular and eggs. Process just until smooth. Pour half cheesecake batter over baked crust. Arrange cherries on top of batter. Add cocoa, chocolate whey protein powder, Da Vinci® Sugar Free Chocolate syrup, whipping cream and Thickening Agent, page 60 to remaining batter; process. Pour over cherries. Bake in 350°F (180°C) oven 35 to 40 minutes, or until center is set. When cooled completely, garnish with whipped cream and additional cherries, if desired. Refrigerate.

CONFECTIONS AND FROSTINGS

JELLY JIGGLE WORMS

These are fun for an induction treat. You'll have to hide them from your children, however, or make them their own batch!

6 envelopes unflavored gelatin
$^1/_2$ cup cold water (125 mL)
2 cups boiling water (500 mL)
$1^3/_4$ cups SPLENDA® Granular (425 mL)
2 envelopes sugarless Kool-Aid®

Yield: 36 servings
1 serving
9.5 calories
1.0 g protein
0.0 g fat
1.3 g carbs

In medium bowl, place gelatin. Stir in $^1/_2$ cup (125 mL) water to soften. Gradually stir in boiling water with wire whisk until dissolved. Gradually stir in SPLENDA® Granular. Pour into 9 x 13-inch (23 x 33 cm) glass dish. Place in refrigerator about 5 minutes to cool. Whisk in Kool-Aid®. Chill until firmly set.

Dip dish in hot water briefly for slightly easier removal. Cut jelly into long strips, beginning from long side of dish. Remove strips as they are cut, to make things easier. Place in plastic container with lid and refrigerate.

Helpful Hints: Cookie cutters may be used to cut shapes, if desired – for example, red hearts for Valentine's Day! These jelly shapes could potentially garnish certain desserts, such as trifles or other puddings, adding interest, texture and flavor.

~~Low-Carb Dieting Tip~~
Switching from a low-fat diet to a higher protein diet can result in building muscle as the previous diet may have been deficient in protein.

CHOCOLATE-DIPPED COCONUT BARS

If chocolate is not enough to dip all bars, drizzle chocolate over remaining bars.
Alternately, make double batch of dipping chocolate; stir nuts into remaining
chocolate and freeze on small, flat baking sheet.

$1^3/_4$ cups unsweetened coconut (425 mL)
$^1/_2$ cup whipping cream (125 mL)
1 envelope unflavored gelatin
$^2/_3$ cup SPLENDA® Granular (150 mL)
1 tsp vanilla extract (5 mL)
Dipping Chocolate:
$1^1/_2$ cups SPLENDA® Granular (375 mL)
6 tbsp skim milk powder, OR (90 mL)
  whole milk powder
$4^1/_2$ tbsp whipping cream (68 mL)
3 tbsp unsalted butter, melted (45 mL)
$1^1/_2$ tbsp water (22 mL)
$^3/_4$ tsp vanilla extract (3 mL)
$1^1/_2$ oz unsweetened baking chocolate (45 g)

Yield: 14 bars	
1 bar	
165.2 calories	
2.3 g protein	
14.3 g fat	
5.8 g carbs	

In food processor food mill or blender, grind $^1/_4$ cup (50 mL) of measured coconut finely. In medium saucepan, place ground coconut, whipping cream and gelatin. Stir and remove from heat as mixture thickens and just starts to boil. Add SPLENDA® Granular and vanilla extract. Stir in remaining coconut. Press firmly into 8-inch (20 cm) square glass baking dish and smooth with back of dessert spoon. Freeze 20 minutes. Cut into 7 bars and cut horizontally through center. Dip bars in Dipping Chocolate below and place on wax paper on cookie sheet. Freeze until chocolate is no longer sticky. Refrigerate.

Dipping Chocolate: In blender or food mill (food processor attachment), blend SPLENDA® Granular and skim milk powder (no blending required with whole milk powdered option) until fine. In medium bowl, combine blended mixture, whipping cream, butter, water and vanilla extract. Stir with wire whisk.

In another cereal bowl, microwave chocolate 2 minutes or until almost completely melted. Stir until chocolate is completely melted. Use soft spatula to scrape all chocolate out of bowl and stir into creamy mixture with wire whisk. If chocolate cools, warm at 10 second intervals in microwave oven, being careful not to overheat, as chocolate will seize and become bitter.

Helpful Hint: 75-80% Fat Fast: 1 bar. (Omit whipping cream and sweetener. Add $^1/_2$ cup (125 mL) Da Vinci® Sugar Free Coconut syrup.)
(134.0 calories, 2.2 g protein, 11.3 g fat (74.1%), 4.7 g carbs)

SMOOTH CHOCOLATE
The variations are good as well.

2 oz light cream cheese, (60 g)
 softened
$^1/_3$ cup Healthy butter, page 62, (75 mL)
 OR unsalted butter, softened
3 tbsp whipping cream (45 mL)
1 tsp vanilla extract (5 mL)
$^1/_2$ cup Confectioner's Sugar Substitute,
 page 91, (125 mL)
$^1/_4$ cup cocoa (50 mL)
$^1/_4$ cup natural whey protein powder (50 mL)

Yield: 64 pieces
1 piece
17.8 calories
0.6 g protein
1.5 g fat
0.4 g carbs

In food processor with sharp blade, or blender, process cream cheese, Healthy Butter, page 62, whipping cream and vanilla extract until smooth. Add Confectioner's Sugar Substitute, page 91, cocoa and whey protein powder; process.

Press into 8-inch (20 cm) square, glass baking dish. Freeze until firm and keep frozen or refrigerate.

Variations: **Incredible Chocolate Frosting:** Omit whey protein powder and cream cheese. *Yield:* Enough for one-layer cake (12 servings). (***2.0 g Carbs***)

Double Chocolate Balls: Use main recipe, omitting cream cheese and whey protein powder and use unsalted butter option, 1 cup (250 mL) Confectioner's Sugar Substitute, page 91, and $^1/_4$ cup (50 mL) SPLENDA® Granular. Form 60 balls and dip in Dipping Chocolate (make a double batch), page 85. Place dipped balls on wax paper. Freeze 15 minutes and refrigerate. (***1.4 g Carbs***)

Stir nuts of choice into remaining chocolate and freeze for a treat later. For half the carbs, simply roll balls in Splenda-sweetened desiccated coconut, walnut crumbs or finely chopped, blanched almonds and place in pretty bonbon cups. Refrigerate.

Helpful Hints: Refrigerated pieces of Smooth Chocolate are like melting moments. Using unsalted butter and freezing the confection will produce harder chocolate.

75-80% Fat Fast: Smooth Chocolate: 10 pieces.
(178.0 calories, 6 g protein, 15 g fat (74.5%), 4 g carbs)

CHOCOLATE-GLAZED PROTEIN BARS

These firm, chewy bars taste wonderful. The Black Forest Bar is the best!

1 oz unsweetened baking chocolate (30 g)
2 tbsp butter (25 mL)
2 tbsp whipping cream (25 mL)
2 tbsp Da Vinci® Sugar Free (25 mL)
  Chocolate syrup
2 tbsp SPLENDA® Granular, (25 mL)
  (optional)
1 tsp vanilla extract (5 mL)
$^3/_4$ cup Chocolate Whey Protein (175 mL)
  (sweetened with sucralose, if possible)
$^3/_4$ cup blanched whole almonds, chopped (175 mL)
$^1/_2$ cup unsweetened coconut (125 mL)
4 SPLENDA® packets

Chocolate Glaze:
1 tbsp unsalted butter (15 mL)
1 tbsp whipping cream (15 mL)
$^1/_4$ tsp vanilla extract (1 mL)
$^1/_2$ cup SPLENDA® Granular (125 mL)
$^1/_2$ oz unsweetened baking chocolate, (15 g)
  melted

Yield: 9 bars
1 bar
222.0 calories
9.0 g protein
19.0 g fat
4.6 g carbs

Melt chocolate and butter in microwave oven 2 minutes. Stir in cream, Da Vinci® Sugar Free Chocolate syrup, SPLENDA® Granular (if using) and vanilla extract until smooth. Add Chocolate Whey Protein, almonds, coconut and SPLENDA®. Combine very well and press into 9 x 5 x 3-inch (2L) loaf pan.

Chocolate Glaze: In cereal bowl, melt butter in microwave oven. Stir in cream, vanilla extract and SPLENDA® Granular until smooth. Stir in chocolate. If necessary, microwave 10 seconds until molten. Spread over surface of mixture in loaf pan. Chill until firm. Cut into 9 bars.

Variation: **Black Forest Protein Bar:** Add 10 pitted cherries, finely chopped. Use $^1/_2$ cup (125 mL) whole almonds, chopped. Add an extra 2 tbsp (25 mL) Chocolate Whey Protein Powder. Omit Da Vinci® Sugar Free Chocolate syrup. For extra moist bars, leave the syrup in the recipe. (*5.5 g Carbs*)

Helpful Hint: **75-80% Fat Fast: Chocolate-Glazed Protein Bar:** 1 bar. (73.0% fat)

CONDENSED MILK

Be prepared for a delicious surprise – very similar in consistency and taste to the real thing! This recipe will be useful in some of your old favorite desserts.

$^1/_3$ cup whipping cream (75 mL)
$^1/_3$ cup butter, softened (75 mL)
3 tbsp water (45 mL)
$^1/_2$ tsp vanilla extract (2 mL)
$^2/_3$ cup SPLENDA® Granular (150 mL)
$^1/_3$ cup whey protein powder (75 mL)
  (natural)
$^1/_3$ cup whole milk powder (75 mL)
$^1/_8$ tsp Thickening Agent, (0.5 mL)
  page 60

> **Yield:** $1^1/_8$ cups (275 mL)
> 1 tbsp (15 mL) per serving
> 65.8 calories
> 2.0 g protein
> 5.6 g fat
> **2.0 g carbs**

In blender, place whipping cream, butter, water, vanilla extract, SPLENDA® Granular, whey protein powder, whole milk powder and Thickening Agent, page 60. Blend until smooth.

Helpful Hints: Skim milk powder may be used instead. Blend in blender to equal $^1/_3$ cup (75 mL).

75-80% Fat Fast: 1 tbsp (15 mL) per serving and up to 4 tbsp (50 mL). (Use only 2 tbsp (25 mL) whipping cream, 1 tbsp (15 mL) water and use $^1/_3$ cup (75 mL) Da Vinci® Sugar Free Caramel or Vanilla Syrup. Omit vanilla extract and SPLENDA® Granular, however, add 1 tbsp (15 mL) for extra sweetness, if desired. Increase Thickening Agent to $^1/_4$ tsp (1 mL). For a superb maple fudge flavor, use Da Vinci® Sugar Free Pancake Syrup.)
1 tbsp (15mL): (53.4 calories, 2.0 g protein, 4.79 g fat (77.8%), 1.0 g carbs)

~~Low-Carb Dieting Tip~~
Stalled for ages? Try shaking things up by carbing up for a couple of days and then launching into induction again for a few days.

ALMOND BUTTER FUDGE

This confection was enjoyed by all in my family.

$1\frac{1}{2}$ cups SPLENDA® Granular (375 mL)
$\frac{1}{2}$ cup Confectioner's Sugar (125 mL)
  Substitute, page 91
3 tbsp whipping cream (45 mL)
2 tbsp unsalted butter, melted (25 mL)
1 tbsp water (15 mL)
$\frac{1}{2}$ tsp vanilla extract (2 mL)
$\frac{1}{8}$ tsp salt (0.5 mL)
$\frac{1}{2}$ cup almond butter (sugar free), (125 mL)
  softened
$\frac{1}{2}$ cup whey protein powder (125 mL)
  (natural flavor)
$\frac{1}{2}$ cup sliced almonds (125 mL)
1 oz cocoa butter, melted (30 g)

Yield: 36 small squares
1 square
63.6 calories
2.3 g protein
5.1 g fat
2.3 g carbs

In medium bowl, combine SPLENDA® Granular, Confectioner's Sugar Substitute, page 91, whipping cream, butter, water, vanilla extract and salt. Use wire whisk to whisk smoothly. Stir in almond butter, whey protein powder and almonds. Stir in cocoa butter.

Press into 8-inch (20 cm) square glass baking dish. Freeze 20 minutes. Cut into squares and refrigerate.

Variation: **Peanut Butter Pecan Fudge:** Use peanut butter (no sugar or salt added) instead of almond butter and chopped pecans instead of sliced almonds. (*2.3 g Carbs*)

~~Low-Carb Dieting Tip~~
Identify your food triggers and avoid them.

DELUXE WHITE CHOCOLATE
My son, Jonathan, says this is the best chocolate I've ever made!

2 x Condensed Milk, page 88
2 oz cocoa butter, melted (60 g)

> **Yield:** 64 pieces
> 1 piece
> 43.9 calories
> 1.2 g protein
> 3.9 g fat
> *1.1 g carbs*

In blender, prepare Condensed Milk, page 88 (double all ingredients). In small cereal bowl, place cocoa butter and melt in microwave oven 3 minutes. Stir to ensure all cocoa butter has melted. Add to condensed milk mixture and blend until smooth. Pour into 8-inch (20 cm) square, glass baking dish. Freeze until firm. Keep frozen. Thaw a few minutes before cutting.

Variations: Stir in blanched, chopped macadamias, hazelnuts or almonds.

Deluxe Milk Chocolate: Omit cocoa butter and use 2 oz (60 g) unsweetened chocolate. Use Chocolate Whey Protein powder instead of Natural Whey Protein powder in Condensed Milk, page 88.
Yield: 64 pieces, 1 piece per serving. (*1.3 g Carbs*)

Helpful Hints: If you have a source for unsweetened Belgian chocolate, that would probably be even nicer. Sometimes I make one layer white chocolate and the top layer milk chocolate. *Yield:* 64 pieces, 1 piece per serving. (*1.2 g Carbs*)

75-80% Fat Fast: 4 pieces per serving.

Deluxe White Chocolate:
(175.6 calories, 4.8 g protein, 15.6 g fat (76.0%), 4.4 g carbs), **OR** with Fat Fast Condensed Milk Recipe (Use Da Vinci® Sugar Free Pancake syrup for a maple fudge flavor that is superb.):
(147.2 calories, 4.4 g protein, 13.6 g fat 81.6%), 2.4 g carbs)

Deluxe Milk Chocolate:
(168.4 calories, 4.8 g protein, 14.8 g fat (76.0 %), 5.2 g carbs), **OR** with Fat Fast Condensed Milk Recipe:
(140.0 calories, 4.8 g protein, 12.4 g fat (77.6%), 2.8 g carbs)

~~Low-Carb Dieting Tip~~
The best time for losing weight is in the first two weeks of your cycle.

RICH CHOCOLATE FROSTING

A delicious frosting for center and top of double-layered cakes.

1 oz unsweetened chocolate, (30 g)
  melted
$^1/_2$ cup Confectioner's Sugar (125 mL)
  Substitute, below
$^1/_4$ cup whipping cream (50 mL)
Confectioner's Sugar Substitute:
2$^1/_4$ cups SPLENDA® Granular (550 mL)
1$^1/_3$ cups whole milk powder (325 mL)
$^1/_2$ cup whey protein powder (125 mL)
  (natural)

> ***Yield:*** 12/16 servings
> 1 serving
> 44.2/ 33.2calories
> 1.4/1.0 g protein
> 3.6/2.7 g fat
> ***2.0/1.5 g carbs***

In cereal bowl, place chocolate. Microwave on high power 2 minutes; stir.

Confectioner's Sugar Substititute: In large bowl, combine SPLENDA® Granular, whole milk powder (See Helpful Hints, page 3, #3) and whey protein powder. Blend in small batches in blender. Stir together in bowl to combine.

Pour Confectioner's Sugar Substitute over melted chocolate. Pour whipping cream over top and stir in all at once, mixing well until smooth. Use to frost double-layered cake or 9 x 13-inch (23 x 33 cm) sheet cake or tube cake.

MILK CHOCOLATE SAUCE

A delicious, rich sauce with many uses.

1 cup whipping cream (250 mL)
$^1/_2$ cup Hot Chocolate Drink (125 mL)
  Mix, *Splendid Low-Carbing*, page 15
1 tbsp unsalted butter (15 mL)
1 tsp vanilla extract (5 mL)

> ***Yield:*** 1$^1/_4$ cups (300 mL)
> 1 tbsp (15 mL) per serving
> 53.1 calories
> 0.9 g protein
> 4.8 g fat
> ***1.8 g carbs***

In nonstick saucepan, stir cream into hot chocolate drink mix gradually. Bring to boil, scraping sides and stirring. Reduce heat and simmer 5 minutes on low heat. Remove from heat. Stir in butter until melted and add vanilla extract.

Helpful Hint: **75-80% Fat Fast:** 1 serving. (to pour over ice cream, for instance). (77.9% fat)

DRIED APPLE AND BANANA SNACKS

Gone are the days, perhaps, when we will eat a whole banana for a snack, however, cut thin slices and dry them in a low oven for a chewy, satisfying snack. It is easier to eat less when "less is more".

2 apples, peeled, cored and thinly sliced
 (24 slices per large apple)
2 bananas, peeled and thinly sliced
 (30 slices per large banana)
$^1/_4$ cup lemon juice (50 mL)
1 tbsp SPLENDA® Granular (15 mL)

Yield: 1 slice apple or banana
1 serving
3.8/3.8 calories
0.0 g/0.0 g protein
0.0 g/0.0 g fat
0.9 g/0.9 g carbs

Prepare fruit. In small bowl, combine lemon juice and SPLENDA® Granular. Dip apple and banana slices in sweetened lemon juice. Place on cake/cookie rack with cookie baking sheet underneath. Bake in 200°F (100°C) oven 1 hour for soft and chewy apples (bananas will still be too soft). Increase heat to 250 (120°C) and bake $1^1/_2$ hours for very chewy apples or 2 hours for crisp apples and bake banana 2 hours at this temperature for chewy banana slices.

Helpful Hints: There will be some lemon juice mixture left over, however, using this amount makes it easier to dip fruit. A food dehydrator may be used instead of the oven.

~~Low-Carb Dieting Tip~~
Emotional eating needs to be identified and addressed.

COOKIES AND SQUARES

PEANUT BUTTER 'N JELLY COOKIES

*I was in the process of making peanut butter cookies, when Ian suggested adding
some Strawberry Jam to the cookies. Thus, these unique thumbprint cookies
were born. I rather like them.*

1 cup peanut butter, (250 mL)
  (smooth or crunchy, no sugar or salt)
1 cup SPLENDA® Granular (250 mL)
1 egg, fork beaten
1 tsp vanilla extract (5 mL)
$^1/_8$ tsp salt (0.5 mL)
8 tsp Strawberry Jam, (40 mL)
  Splendid Low-Carbing, page 91

Yield: 30 cookies
1 cookie
56.2 calories
2.0 g protein
4.3 g fat
2.2 g carbs

In cereal bowl, place peanut butter and soften in microwave oven 45 seconds. In
medium bowl, combine peanut butter, SPLENDA® Granular, egg, vanilla extract
and salt. Form dough into 1-inch (2.5 cm) smooth balls. Place on greased cookie
sheet and press thumb or forefinger in middle of each cookie. Fill each cookie
carefully with $^1/_4$ tsp (1 mL) Strawberry Jam, *Splendid Low-Carbing*, page 91.
Bake 10 to 12 minutes in 350°F (180°C) oven. Allow to cool before removing
cookies. Store in refrigerator.

Variations: **Plain Peanut Butter Cookies:** Place balls of dough on greased
cookie sheet. Press with fork to flatten. Omit Strawberry Jam. (***2.0 g Carbs***)

Peanut Butter Pecan Cookies: Add $^1/_2$ cup (125 mL) chopped pecans.
(***2.3 g Carbs***)

Helpful Hint: **75-80% Fat Fast: Plain Peanut Butter Cookies:** 2 cookies.
(110.4 calories, 4.0 g protein, 8.6 g fat (70.5%), 2.0 g carbs)

~~Low-Carb Dieting Tip~~
*Reread your low-carb diet book every now and then to inspire you and remind
you of things you may have forgotten.*

93

GINGERSNAPS

Very close to the real thing! Tons of cookies with a long shelf life.

$2^1/_4$ cups Whey Ultimate (550 mL)
  Bake Mix, page 67
1 cup SPLENDA® Granular (250 mL)
$^3/_4$ cup shortening OR butter, (175 mL)
  softened
*3 tbsp DaVinci® Sugar Free (45 mL)
  Caramel Syrup
1 tbsp molasses (15 mL)
1 egg
2 tsp ground ginger (10 mL)
1 tsp ground cinnamon (5 mL)
1 tsp baking soda (5 mL)
$^1/_4$ tsp ground cloves (1 mL)
$^1/_4$ tsp ground nutmeg (1 mL)
2 tbsp SPLENDA® Granular (25 mL)

Yield: 54 cookies
1 cookie
51.0 calories
1.8 g protein
3.9 g fat
2.1 g carbs

In large mixing bowl, place half Whey Ultimate Bake Mix, page 67. Add SPLENDA® Granular, shortening or butter, DaVinci® Sugar Free Caramel Syrup, molasses, egg, ginger, cinnamon, baking soda, cloves and nutmeg. Beat with electric mixer until thoroughly combined. Beat in remaining bake mix. Shape cookie dough into 1-inch (2.5 cm) balls. Place 2-inches (5 cm) apart on ungreased cookie sheets.

On small plate, spread SPLENDA® Granular. Dip fork in SPLENDA® Granular and press dough ball with tines of fork, one way, dip again and then criss-cross the other way. Bake in 300°F (150°C) oven 18 to 20 minutes, or until browned underneath. Cool on wire racks.

Helpful Hints: *If you don't have DaVinci® Sugar Free Caramel Syrup, use any low-carb syrup you have available. It is possible to omit molasses and add an extra tablespoon (15 mL) syrup. These cookies will most likely work well with Soy Ultimate Bake Mix as well, however, they were tested with the above bake mix.

A regular sugar-filled Gingersnap cookie has approximately 11 g carbs!

~~Low-Carb Dieting Tip~~
Reading low-carb success stories is a great motivator.

ALMOND BUTTER PECAN COOKIES

Or use peanut butter and omit almond extract (2.2 g Carbs).

$^1/_2$ cup almond butter, (125 mL)
$^1/_2$ cup whipping cream (125 mL)
$^1/_2$ cup chopped pecans, OR (125 mL)
   chopped almonds
$^1/_2$ cup SPLENDA® Granular (125 mL)
$^1/_2$ cup Ultimate Bake Mix, (125 mL)
   page 67
1 tsp baking powder (5 mL)
1 tsp vanilla extract (5 mL)
$^1/_4$ tsp almond extract (1 mL)

Yield: 24 cookies
1 cookie
62.3 calories
1.6 g protein
5.3 g fat
2.5 g carbs

In medium bowl, combine almond butter, cream, pecans or almonds, SPLENDA® Granular, Ultimate Bake Mix, page 67, baking powder, vanilla extract and almond extract.

Form into 24 equal-sized balls {slightly bigger than 1 inch (2.5 cm)}. Place on greased cookie sheet. Flatten each ball in cross-cross pattern with fork. Bake in 375°F (190°C) oven 10 to 12 minutes, or until brown underneath.

CHOCOLATE CHIP COOKIES

An all-time favorite gone low-carb! Double recipe, if desired.

$^1/_2$ cup butter, softened (125 mL)
1 egg
2 tsp vanilla extract (10 mL)
1 cup Ultimate Bake Mix, (250 mL)
   page 67
$^3/_4$ cup SPLENDA® Granular (175 mL)
$^1/_2$ tsp baking soda (2 mL)
$^1/_8$ tsp salt (0.5 mL)
$^3/_4$ cup sugar free chocolate chips (175 mL)

Yield: 30 cookies
1 cookie
59.2 calories
1.4 g protein
5.3 g fat
1.9 g carbs

In small bowl with electric mixer, beat butter briefly, adding egg and vanilla extract. Beat. In small bowl, combine Ultimate Bake Mix, page 67, SPLENDA® Granular, baking soda and salt. Add to mixer; beat. Stir in chocolate chips.

Using slightly rounded 1$^1/_2$ tsp (7 mL) measuring spoon, drop cookie dough onto greased baking sheet. Bake in 375°F (190°C) oven 8 minutes, or until browned underneath.

LEMON SQUARES

My version of these timeless, very popular squares. Make a double batch as these go quickly!

Almond Crust:
$^3/_4$ cup ground almonds (175 mL)
3 tbsp Ultimate Bake Mix, (45 mL)
  page 67
3 tbsp SPLENDA® Granular (45 mL)
3 tbsp butter, melted (45 mL)
1 egg yolk

Filling:
2 eggs
$^1/_2$ cup SPLENDA® Granular (125 mL)
$^1/_4$ cup fresh lemon juice (50 mL)
3 tbsp sour cream (45 mL)
1 tbsp vital wheat gluten (15 mL)
1 tsp finely grated lemon rind (5 mL)
$^1/_4$ tsp baking powder (1 mL)
$1^1/_2$ tsp ground almonds, (7 mL)
  toasted

Yield: 25 squares
1 square
38.7 calories
1.9 g protein
2.7 g fat
1.9 g carbs

Almond Crust: In small bowl, combine ground almonds, Ultimate Bake Mix, page 67, SPLENDA® Granular, butter and egg yolk. Press into 8-inch (20 cm) square glass baking dish. Bake in 350°F (180°C) oven 10 minutes.

Filling: In another small bowl, beat eggs with fork until frothy. Stir in SPLENDA® Granular, lemon juice and sour cream. Add vital wheat gluten, lemon rind and baking powder; stir. Pour over crust and bake in 350°F (180°C) oven 20 minutes, or until set. Meanwhile toast ground almonds in small nonstick baking pan until golden. Sprinkle over baked Lemon Squares. Cool on wire rack 10 minutes. Cut into squares.

~~Low-Carb Dieting Tip~~
One should not eat a diet that is both high in carbohydrate and fat.

DEEP DARK BROWNIES

So good! These brownies are best served at room temperature.

1 cup Protein Bake Mix, p. 68 (250 mL)
$^{1}/_{2}$ cup cocoa (125 mL)
24 SPLENDA® packets, OR
  1 cup SPLENDA® Granular (250 mL)
$^{1}/_{2}$ cup SPLENDA® Granular (125 mL)
1 cup unsalted butter, melted (250 mL)
6 eggs, fork beaten.
2 tsp vanilla extract (10 mL)
1 cup sugar free chocolate chips (250 mL)

Yield: 54 brownies
1 brownie
63.8 calories
2.4 g protein
5.7 g fat
1.2 g carbs

In medium bowl, combine Protein Bake Mix, page 68, cocoa, SPLENDA® and SPLENDA® Granular. Add butter, eggs and vanilla extract. Stir to combine well. Fold in chocolate chips. Scoop batter evenly into greased 9 x 13-inch (23 x 33 cm) glass baking dish. Bake in 350°F (180°C) oven 20 minutes, or until cake tester inserted in cake part comes out clean. Do not overbake.

MILK CHOCOLATE BROWNIES

Decadent! Can one ever have too many brownie recipes to try? Best chilled. If using shortening option, purchase non-hyrdogenated brand.

Dipping Chocolate, page 85
$^{1}/_{3}$ cup shortening, OR butter (75 mL)
  softened (unsalted)
$^{1}/_{4}$ cup DaVinci® Sugar Free, (50 mL)
  Chocolate Syrup
2 eggs, fork beaten
1 tsp vanilla extract (5 mL)
$^{1}/_{2}$ cup Whey Ultimate Bake Mix, (125 mL)
  page 67 using ground hazelnuts
$^{1}/_{4}$ cup Chocolate Whey Protein (50 mL)
1 tsp baking powder (5 mL)
$^{1}/_{8}$ tsp salt (0.5 mL)
1 cup sugar free chocolate chips (250 mL)

Yield: 54 brownies
1 brownie
48.2 calories
1.1 g protein
4.3 g fat
1.6 g carbs

In medium bowl, prepare Dipping Chocolate, page 85. Stir in shortening and DaVinci® Sugar Free Chocolate Syrup until well combined. Add eggs and vanilla extract. Stir in Whey Ultimate Bake Mix, Chocolate Whey Protein, baking powder and salt. Fold in chocolate chips. Scoop batter evenly into 9 x 13-inch (23 x 33 cm) glass baking dish. Bake in 350°F (180°C) oven 20 minutes.

CANDY SQUARES

Absolutely decadent-tasting, chewy squares. Your friends will never guess they're actually low-carb.

Condensed Milk, page 88 (175 mL)
1 cup ground almonds (250 mL)
1 cup chocolate chips, (250 mL)
 (sugar free)
$^1/_2$ cup fine desiccated coconut, (125 mL)
 (unsweetened)
$^1/_2$ cup chopped pecans (125 mL)
$^1/_4$ cup almond butter, (50 mL)
2 tbsp SPLENDA® Granular (25 mL)
1 egg, fork beaten

Yield: 36 squares
1 square
87.2 calories
2.6 g protein
7.7 g fat
2.3 g carbs

In medium bowl, combine Condensed Milk, page 88, ground almonds, chocolate chips, coconut, pecans, almond butter, SPLENDA® Granular and egg. Stir to combine well. Pour into greased 9-inch (23 cm) square, glass baking dish. Bake in 350°F (180°C) oven 20 to 25 minutes, or until set.

Variation: **No Bake Candy Squares:** Use $^1/_2$ cup (125 mL) sliced almonds instead of chopped pecans and $^3/_4$ cup (175 mL) Condensed Milk, page 88. Omit egg. In medium bowl, combine all ingredients. Press into 9-inch (23 cm) square, glass baking dish. Chill. *Yield:* 36 squares. (*2.0 g carbs*)

Helpful Hint: If you're having trouble locating sugar free chocolate chips, chop sugar free chocolate bars of choice in food processor into coarse chips.

~~Low-Carb Dieting Tip~~
Snacking frequently, stalls many people, as insulin levels are kept higher. Did you know, typically, men snack less frequently than women?

CHOCOLATE ALMOND BISCOTTI

These rusk-like cookies didn't last more than a day, as we all loved them!

$^1/_3$ cup butter, softened (75 mL)
2 cups Ultimate Bake Mix, (500 mL)
  page 67
$^2/_3$ cup SPLENDA® Granular (150 mL)
2 eggs
1 tbsp baking powder (15 mL)
1 tsp vanilla extract (5 mL)
$1^1/_2$ cups slivered almonds, (375 mL)
  finely chopped
1 fork beaten egg yolk
1 tbsp water (15 mL)

Drizzling Chocolate:
1 tbsp unsalted butter (15 mL)
1 tbsp whipping cream (15 mL)
$^1/_4$ tsp vanilla extract (1 mL)
$^1/_2$ cup SPLENDA® Granular (125 mL)
$^1/_2$ oz unsweetened baking chocolate, melted (15 g)

Yield: 32 Biscotti
1 Biscotti
105.6 calories
3.9 g protein
8.4 g fat
3.5 g carbs

In food processor or electric mixer, process butter. Add half Ultimate Bake Mix, page 67; process. Add SPLENDA® Granular, eggs, baking powder and vanilla extract. Process until thoroughly combined. Add remaining Ultimate Bake Mix, page 67 and almonds. Turn dough out on clean surface. Divide dough in half.

Shape each portion into 9-inch (23 cm) loaf, approximately 2-inches (5 cm) wide. Place loaves several inches apart on lightly greased cookie sheet. In small bowl, combine egg yolk and water. Brush over loaves. Bake in 375°F (190°C) oven 25 minutes. Cool on cookie sheet half an hour. Cut each loaf diagonally into 16 slices. Lay slices, cut side down, on ungreased cookie sheets. Bake in 325°F (160°C) oven 10 minutes. Flip each cookie and bake another 8 minutes, or until golden brown and crisp. Cool on wire racks. Drizzle chocolate over biscotti.

Chocolate Drizzle: In small bowl, melt butter in microwave oven. Stir in cream, vanilla extract and SPLENDA® Granular until smooth. Stir in chocolate. If necessary, microwave 10 seconds.

Helpful Hints: Instead of Drizzling Chocolate, one could melt 100 g (3.5 oz) bar sugar free (maltitol) chocolate and stir in 2 tbsp (25 mL) shortening (non-hydrogenated) or butter. Dip one side of Biscotti. (**3.3 g Carbs**) Some of the almonds may be replaced with sugar free chocolate chips. Hazelnuts may be used instead of almonds, if desired.

INDEX

A

H

HAM AND CHEESE QUICHE 24
HAMBURGER BUNS 66
HAMBURGER SOUP 15
HEALTHY BUTTER 62
HORSERADISH SHRIMP DIP 10
HOT CHOCOLATE 5
HOT DOG BUNS 66

I

ICE CREAMS AND PUDDINGS 69

ANY FLAVOR ICE CREAM CUSTARD 71
ANY FLAVOR PANNA COTTA 72
ANY FLAVOR YOGURT JELLY 70
BLENDER COCONUT CUSTARD PIE 72
CHOCOLATE ICE CREAM CUSTARD 71
CHOCOLATE MOUSSE 80
COCONUT CHOCOLATE MOUSSE 69
COCONUT MOUSSE 69
CRÈME CARAMEL CUSTARD 72
CRÈME FRAICHE 70
FRENCH VANILLA ICE CREAM CUSTARD 71
LINDA'S ICE CREAM CUSTARD 71
STRAWBERRY ICE CREAM CUSTARD 71
VANILLA CREAM JELLY 73
INCREDIBLE CHOCOLATE FROSTING 86

J

JAMAICAN DRUMSTICKS 39
JELLY JIGGLE WORMS 84
JERK SAUCE 39
JUMBO RICOTTA PANCAKE 29

L

LEMON LAMB ROAST 32
LEMON PARSLEY DRESSING 36
LEMON RICOTTA MUFFINS 65
LEMON SAUCE 44
LEMON SQUARES 96
LEMONADE CONCENTRATE 7
LINDA'S ICE CREAM CUSTARD 71
LOAF PAN BREADS 66

M

MANDARIN SPINACH SALAD 18
MAPLE WALNUT MOCK DANISH 26
MARMALADE 59
MAYONNAISE 58
MAYONNAISE SALAD DRESSING 62

MEAT 30

APPLE MEAT LOAF 34
APPLE CURRY MEAT LOAF 34
BAVARIAN CROCK-POT ROAST 36
BEEF STEW 30
CABBAGE ROLLS 31
CHEESE TACOS 33
CURRIED BEEF STEW 30
LEMON LAMB ROAST 32
SIRLOIN STEAK WITH LEMON PARSLEY 36
SPICY SLOPPY JOES 35
TACO DOG 35
MILD CURRY POWDER 61
MILK CHOCOLATE BROWNIES 97
MILK CHOCOLATE SAUCE 91

MISCELLANEOUS 58

BARBECUE SAUCE 61
BUTTER SAUCE 76
CHEESE SAUCE 50
CREAMY MUSTARD SAUCE 60
CURRY POWDER 61
FRUIT SALSA 48
GRAVY 32
HEALTHY BUTTER 62
JERK SAUCE 39
LEMON PARSLEY DRESSING 36
LEMON SAUCE 44
MARMALADE 59
MAYONNAISE 58
MAYONNAISE SALAD DRESSING 62
MILD CURRY POWDER 61
SWEET-SOUR DRESSING 19
TACO MIX 33
THICKENING AGENT 60
TOMATO-CHILI SAUCE 31
WALNUT TOPPING 76
YOGURT SAUCE 47
MUSHROOM MOZZARELLA BAKE 54

N

NO BAKE CANDY SQUARES 98
NUTTY FRENCH TOAST 28

O

OVEN ZUCCHINI FRIES 55

P

PEANUT BUTTER MOCK DANISH 26
PEANUT BUTTER 'N JELLY COOKIES 93
PEANUT BUTTER PECAN COOKIES 93
PEANUT BUTTER PECAN FUDGE 89
PEPPER CHUNKS AND STEWED TOMATO 56

More HELPFUL HINTS (From Splendid Low-Carbing)

1. Usable Carbs or Net Carbs = carbohydrates per serving minus the fiber. The reason for this is that the value for the carbohydrates calculated is actually the carbohydrates plus the fiber. Most Fiber is indigestible or poorly absorbed. The carbohydrate values shown in all the recipes and their variations are actually the usable carbs, so the math has already been done for you. All recipes are below 10 grams carbohydrate; most are below 5 grams and many are below 3 grams.

2. Serving Sizes or Yield - Optional ingredients were not included in the nutritional analysis. If a recipe calls for one ingredient OR another one, the analysis is based on the first ingredient. If the carbs differ significantly when using the second ingredient, you will usually find the analysis in the variations or helpful hints below the recipe. Sometimes dessert serving sizes are slightly smaller than standard sizes.

3. Shelf Life - of goodies made with SPLENDA® Granular is short, especially in hot weather. Refrigerate baked goods, including breads, after a day. Remove cakes, etc. two hours before serving. Most baked goods will freeze well for one month. Refrigerate sealed jams or chutneys 6 months or freeze for longer storage.

4. Crusts - were the bad guys in the old low-fat days and are still the bad guys today on the low-carb diet. In the old days, crusts added extra fat; nowadays it is the extra carbohydrates they add, which concern us. For many of the desserts, it is possible to omit the crust, if desired, or simply sprinkle a pie dish with a light dusting of ground or finely chopped, toasted nuts. Typically, my crusts add no more than 1 to 3 grams of carbohydrate per serving.

5. Thickening Agent - This agent is primarily used to thicken sauces, instant blender puddings, frostings and toppings. Sprinkle over hot sauces gradually and whisk in. Use this agent in very small quantities to prevent that gummy feel. Thickening Agent, soy flour, cocoa, vegetable gums and gelatin will all serve to cut sweetness to some degree in baking. Vegetable gums, while listed as containing carbohydrate, are composed mostly of indigestible fiber.

6. Bake Mixes - Bake Mixes, which you can make yourself, are the secret to many of my recipes. They are not a cup-for-cup substitution for white flour, however, see Ultimate Bake Mix, page 67 for that purpose. The simple techniques I employed in the recipes will soon become apparent. Soon you will be able to modify some of your own favorite recipes. In breads, the Bake Mixes impart a wonderful rich, nutty flavor. Whole spelt flour or whole wheat pastry flour or whole wheat flour may be substituted for spelt flour. The reason I used spelt flour (see #14) was not only for the gluten content and the fact that it is biologically unrelated to wheat, but also for its higher protein content and its taste. I cannot stand an obvious "soy" taste, and if I had only used soy flour, taste would have gone out the window, in my opinion. There is an alternative – Whey Ultimate Bake Mix (soy-free) - that is wonderful in baking. It has about the same number of carbs as the Bake Mix, which uses soy flour, the only difference occurring in breads where the extra soy flour in the recipes is replaced with spelt flour. This accounts for about 0.7 grams carbohydrate extra per serving. Also some breads made with Whey Ultimate Bake Mix don't rise quite as high (but almost), however, they have a different flavor, and are quite crusty, which you may prefer. If you do a lot of baking, whip up a double batch of the Bake Mix of your choice for convenience. Store in an airtight container at room temperature or in the refrigerator or freezer for longer storage. Ultimate Bake Mix may be substituted for any of the other bake mixes. Bake mixes with whey protein powder sometimes create a drier baked product. To counteract this, replace some of the butter in a recipe with light-tasting olive oil and, if possible, replace some of the liquid in the recipe with whipping cream.

7. Ultimate Bake Mix - This is a cup-for-cup all-purpose and cake flour substitute for convenience and to make the low-carb life-style even more livable. See page 67 for more details. It may be used to reduce the carbohydrates in my books, *Splendid Desserts* and *More Splendid Desserts* by 50 to 65% (for example, in Glazed Lemon Loaf, *More Splendid Desserts*, the carbs are reduced by 12 grams per slice; a 64% reduction!). This bake mix tastes like the real thing and usually works in muffin, loaf and cake recipes without a problem (adjust liquid by adding gradually until the right batter consistency is achieved). I cannot guarantee the results in cookies; however, I've had success with most cookie recipes. Again, add liquid cautiously and see #10 for suggestions re using Whey Ultimate Bake Mix. I do know this bake mix will not work in the "koeksister" recipe in *More Splendid Desserts*. However, do remember, if one indulges in too many slices of a cake made with this bake mix, a water weight gain is inevitable, as ones's glycogen stores are replaced. Go back to strict low-carbing for a day or two and the water should come off. It is best to eat a slice of cake after a balanced meal, in which case you should see hardly any after-effects on the scale. Do not snack on it at various times of the day, as the carbs add up quickly, and the extra insulin output will make your appetite soar. Would you, in the old low-fat days, have indulged in high-fat, calorific cakes every other day? Of course, not! View cakes, etc. made with the Ultimate Bake Mix similarly on our diet; as occasional treats, to be enjoyed in moderation.

8. Breads - Vital wheat gluten can vary from 75 to 80% gluten. I used Bob's Red Mill Vital Wheat Gluten (see #17), available in Canada and America (also at www.bobsredmill.com and www.CarbSmart.com). My breads work best (rise higher) with this percentage gluten. The dough typically should look fairly moist as it is mixing and kneading. Baking can sometimes be a bit of an art form. Besides the minor differences in products coming from different companies, bread machines differ, temperatures can make a difference and other factors such as altitude could have an influence on your baking. My bread machine is over 10 years old (Hitachi Model HB-B201) and makes a large, broad cottage-style loaf. When dough is elastic and needs to be rolled out, allow to rest under towel 10 minutes at a time between rolling. The yeast eats sugar in bread recipes.

By keeping all other parameters the same in the Bran Bread Machine Bread, one can play with the variables, $^1/_2$ cup (125 mL) wheat bran and $^1/_3$ cup (75 mL) soy flour, by substituting other ingredients. For instance, one could use oat bran instead of wheat bran and spelt flour, whole wheat pastry flour, triticale flour, rye flour, oat flour, amaranth flour, quinoa flour or any other flour instead of soy flour. The carbs will not be significantly affected. If one uses spelt flour instead of soy flour, the carbs go up by 0.7 grams per serving. However, if one also replaces the wheat bran with flour of any kind, the carbs will go up by approximately 2 to 3 grams per serving. Whey breads are milder tasting and form a nice crust. They also toast very well. Soy breads are moist in texture and rise to the top in the bread machine.

9. Spelt Flour - For some folks, this may be the first time you've heard of this complex carbohydrate flour, which is lately being re-discovered. All-purpose, whole wheat flour, whole wheat pastry flour or whole grain spelt flour may be substituted for unbleached spelt flour, if desired. Many people have wheat allergies or find that wheat is a trigger for carbohydrate cravings. Spelt was grown in Europe more than 9000 years ago according to modern research. Spelt flour (www.purityfoods.com) was used in Old Testament Bible times (Exodus 9:31-32 and Ezekiel 4:9) and is biologically unrelated to wheat flour. It does contain some gluten, however, it is a different quality to wheat gluten. It is loaded with vitamins and minerals, contains a complex carbohydrate and has a higher protein content than wheat flour. It tastes better than most other grains and is suitable for both cooking and baking. *Note:* Where small amounts of spelt flour are used in a recipe, as an alternative to soy flour, use vital wheat gluten instead, if desired.

10. Soy Flour and other soy products - This relatively low-carbohydrate and inexpensive flour is very useful to the low-carb dieter! Just as with any other product, which is very popular (even SPLENDA® Granular), there are those who do not like it. Personally, I believe "most things in moderation" is a good motto. One does not see too many overweight Asian people, besides Asian women have a tremendously easier time of menopause than we Western women do. Soy flour has been touted as a wonder food to help ease menopause, build bones and even prevent breast cancer, but then I've heard completely opposing views. For now, the overall consensus is the apparent benefits (many studies done) of soy products far outweigh any negatives. On the most negative site on the web regarding soy flour, the apparent safe level for soy flour per day that they recommend is approximately 3 tbsp (45 mL). That would probably amount to a couple of slices of one of my breads, which contain some soy flour. However, if you have a thyroid problem, the consensus is that it is best to avoid soy products. Wherever possible, I have provided alternatives.

There may be some confusion about the different soy products used in this book. I've used low-fat soy flour in my recipes (as opposed to full-fat soy flour), because I preferred the taste, and because it is even more concentrated in protein. Soy powder has a finer texture and may be substituted in crusts and cheesecakes where small amounts of soy flour are used. It tends to have a milder flavor than soy flour and produces a slightly less dense texture in baked goods. However, soy flour is better suited to mixing with nut flours and other flours. Look for organic low-fat soy flour, which has a rich, mild flavor. Not all soy flours are made equal. Shop around to find a mild-tasting low-fat soy flour. It may take some time to get accustomed to the taste of soy flour; however, I cannot detect an obvious soy taste in any of my recipes, as I use it judiciously and in small quantities. There are one or two recipes, which call for soy protein isolate. This product has virtually zero carbs. It may not be substituted for soy flour or soy powder. Look for these products at upscale health food stores and in larger grocery chains, as well as online.

Be careful with cookie recipes, especially ones where most of the moisture comes from butter. Soy flour can make cookies dry and powdery tasting. To correct this problem, try replacing some of the butter with whipping cream. Wherever dough needs to be kneaded on a lightly floured surface, use soy protein isolate or whey protein powder.

11. Whey Protein Powder - This is the popular alternative to soy flour, which I employed in my recipes, however, it is quite expensive. One can get a club card and discounts at most health food stores and I typically buy mine on sale. Some health food stores have whey protein powders available in bulk bins (verify they are sugar free). Sometimes that works out cheaper, but not always. I used natural whey protein powder without any sweeteners added. The two brands I used were Supreme Supplements Whey Protein (Canadian brand, Phone: (888) 834-7760) and Ultimate Nutrition Inc., ProStar Whey (American brand, Fax: (860) 793-5006, www.ultimatenutrition.com).

12. Vital Wheat Gluten - This product is wheat flour with the starch removed and is usually 75 to 80% gluten (natural protein in the wheat endosperm). I used Bob's Red Mill Gluten (www.bobsredmill.com, Natural Foods Inc., Milwaukie, Oregon), which is a high quality vital wheat gluten. Gluten flour, on the other hand, is half vital wheat gluten and cannot be substituted for vital wheat gluten. My program lists $1/4$ cup (50 mL) or 38 grams (1.3 oz) vital wheat gluten as 6.0 g carbs, whereas gluten flour has 16.2 grams carbs.

13. SPLENDA® Granular - Most of you will be familiar with this low-calorie sweetener. We've been using it in Canada for almost a decade before FDA approval in the States and, after developing 4 Splenda® Cookbooks, I'm very familiar with its nuances in cooking and baking. Keep in mind SPLENDA® Granular weighs about $^1/_8$ as much as sugar, and this does affect volume and texture in some baking recipes.

Caramelizing, or producing the same effects as brown sugar, for instance, chewiness in cookies, are not possible to my knowledge. Some adjustment of ingredients in recipes where sugar provides texture and volume will be necessary.

Sucralose, created from sugar, has no carbohydrates or calories. The sugar molecule was altered in such a way that the body no longer recognizes it. Maltodextrin, a carbohydrate derived from corn, is a filler used to help the product measure cup-for-cup like sugar. The carb content in 1 cup (250 mL) SPLENDA® Granular is 24 grams. Sucralose is inert and remains stable at the high baking temperatures.

Some people have raised the concern that maltodextrin features higher on the glycemic index scale than sugar! However, it all depends on the quantity you ingest per serving of a dessert. If one were to eat a pound of maltodextrin, one would be in trouble, however, the way Splenda is formulated from sucralose and maltodextrin, this results in very little weight being imparted by maltodextrin. In fact, 1 cup (250 mL) SPLENDA® Granular weighs 26 grams (almost nothing!) and 1 cup of sugar weighs 226 grams. Therefore, one serving of dessert sweetened with, say, 1 cup (250 mL) SPLENDA® Granular has very little maltodextrin in it, and it will have very little impact on glycemic reactions, however, the opposite is true for a sugar-sweetened dessert, which is quite high in carbohydrates and calories too.

It is easy to replace SPLENDA® Granular (and reduce carbs) with Da Vinci® Gourmet Sugar Free Syrup (sucralose-sweetened), where there is already liquid in the recipe that can be replaced. The carb breakdown for various amounts of SPLENDA® Granular may be found on page 19. It is possible to use other brands of Sugar Free Syrup, such as Torani's® or Nature's Flavors®, however, my choice is Da Vinci® Sugar Free Syrups. It is also possible to substitute SPLENDA® Granular with any other granulated sweetener that is suitable for baking. If liquid SPLENDA® becomes available, this product may also be used instead of the granulated sweetener. Kool-Aid® flavoring or flavored extracts, water and SPLENDA® Granular may be used instead of sugar free syrups.My family has probably been the biggest consumer of SPLENDA® Granular on this planet! A decade later, we're not showing any apparent adverse effects.

14. Flax Seed - This is another wonder food which everyone is talking about and which I use in several of my recipes. It is the world's richest source of Omega-3, an essential fatty acid. It is also rich in Omega-6, another essential fatty acid.

Flax seeds are nature's "Tomoxifen" (anti-cancer drug) latest studies reveal. Also called linseed, it is a good source of fiber.

15. *Eggs* - Unless otherwise specified, large eggs were used.

16. *Yogurt, Buttermilk and Kefir* - Happily, the Go-Diet authors, Jack Goldberg and Karen O'Mara changed my outlook with regard to these products. The live cultures such as lactobacillus are hugely beneficial to your health in many ways (see pages 21 and 48 of their book), not the least of which is helping combat yeast overgrowth, promoting colon health and boosting the immune system. According to laboratory studies, 1 cup (250 mL) plain yogurt contains only about 4 grams of carbohydrate, since these live bacteria have changed the lactose into lactic acid, and this is not taken into account in the nutritional analysis. Daily consumption of yogurt is therefore highly recommended. I used this information to calculate the carbohydrate values in applicable recipes.

17. *Almonds* - are a most versatile nut! To grind nuts, a coffee/nut grinder will produce a finer product than a blender would. Commercially available ground almonds are very convenient. However, if you're grinding blanched almonds from scratch, then keep this in mind: 1 tbsp (15 mL) blanched almonds produces about 1.3 tbsp (20 mL) ground almonds. Therefore, if you need $^2/_3$ cup (150 mL) ground almonds, divide that by 1.3 to arrive at approximately $^1/_2$ cup (125 mL) blanched almonds, ground. When working in reverse order, multiply by 1.3. This rule does not apply to most other nuts. Refrigerate or freeze ground almonds and other nuts, if not using frequently, to keep fresh longer.

18. *Lower Fat Alternatives* - To lower fat content, half-and-half cream may be substituted in many cases, where whipping cream has been used. You can get the same result and the same carbohydrate content by mixing half whipping cream and half 2% or 1% milk in a jug. This may work out cheaper than especially buying half-and-half cream. Lower fat alternatives may often be substituted.

19. *Healthy Butter* - Do use this recipe, if you find you like it. It saves money and it is so useful to have in the refrigerator, as it spreads like soft margarine and tastes like butter. It is higher in monounsaturated fats and lower in saturated fats. Use an olive oil without a distinct flavor to prevent overpowering the butter taste.

20. *To further reduce carbs:* - Many of the recipes, especially confections, will be fine using 8 SPLENDA® packets per 1 cup (250 mL) SPLENDA® Granular. That is 8 g carbs versus 24 g (reduced by two thirds). The sweetening power of the packets is greater than the granular version. The results are less predictable in baking, plus it's really awkward opening so many packets. The SPLENDA® packets are available in Costco and Sam's Club at a good price.

ORDERING INFORMATION

(All Prices below include S&H via USPS media mail)

SPLENDID LOW-CARBING $24 US

MORE SPLENDID LOW-CARBING $17 US

SPLENDID LOW-CARBING FOR LIFE (Volume-1) $17 US

Or all 3 "SPLENDID LOW-CARBING" cookbooks $55 US

Also, you can still order **SPLENDID DESSERTS** $13 US

And **MORE SPLENDID DESSERTS** $15 US

Or order Both of these "SPLENDID DESSERTS" cookbooks $26 US

Any/All of these books can be ordered by MAIL simply by
sending your selections and a check, money order or Bank draft to:

Aurum Group
PO Box 907,
Great Falls, MT
USA 59403

BUT, please allow 4-8 weeks for delivery when ordering by mail!

Or *save money* and get these books much sooner by ordering SECURELY online from:
www.sweety.com or www.Low-Carb.us *Also look for this "Splendid" series of
cookbooks to be available (soon) through / on* **Amazon.com**'s very popular website .

Please note: Recipes in *Splendid Desserts* and *More Splendid Desserts* can now be
adapted to suit a low-carb lifestyle by using the Ultimate Bake Mix, page 67 of *More
Splendid Low-Carbing* or by requesting a copy of this recipe. As well, any "Special
order" inquiries can be sent to the above address or emailed to **Desserts@Sweety.com**

---

(1) Although I have satisfied myself concerning the safety of SPLENDA®, it is up to each
individual to decide that independently. For more information on the safety of SPLENDA® Low-
Calorie Sweetener, call 1-800-561-0070 in Canada or write to SPLENDA® Information Center,
P.O. Box 1390, Guelph, Ontario, Canada N1K 1A5, or in the U.S.A. write to SPLENDA®
Information Center, 501 George Street, JH305, New Brunswick, NJ, USA 08901.

(2) SPLENDA® Low-Calorie Sweetener is the registered trademark of McNeil-PPC, Inc. Neither
McNeil Specialty Products nor McNeil Consumer Products Company have been involved in the
development, production or distribution of this cookbook.

(3) Da Vinci® Gourmet is the registered trademark of Da Vinci Gourmet, Ltd. They have
not been involved in the development or production of this cookbook.
